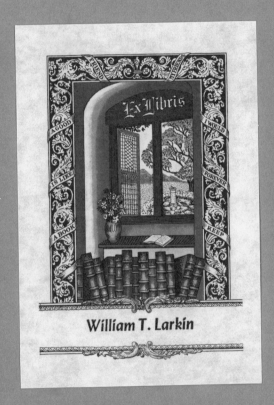

A FRIEND IS LIKE A GOOD BOOK

Ex Libris

I WOULD FOREVER KEEP

William T. Larkin

PILOTS' DIRECTIONS

THE AMERICAN LAND
AND LIFE SERIES

Edited by Wayne Franklin

THE TRANSCONTINENTAL AIRWAY

AND ITS HISTORY

PREFACE BY WAYNE FRANKLIN

University of Iowa Press 🌵 Iowa City

EDITED BY WILLIAM M. LEARY

PILOTS'
DIRECTIONS

University of Iowa Press,
Iowa City 52242
Copyright © 1990 by the
University of Iowa
All rights reserved
Printed in the United States
of America
First edition, 1990

Design by Richard Hendel

Printed on acid-free paper

The transcontinental air route map,
by R. E. G. Davies, is reprinted from
Aerial Pioneers, courtesy of
the Smithsonian Institution Press.
The photograph of Otto Praeger is
reproduced courtesy of the Praeger
family, and the photograph of
James P. Murray bringing the mail to
Rock Springs is courtesy of Mrs.
James P. Murray. All other
photographs are courtesy of the
National Air and Space Museum.
Pilots' Directions was originally
published by the Government
Printing Office in 1921.

Library of Congress
Cataloging-in-Publication Data
Pilots' directions: the transcontinen-
tal airway and its history/edited by
William M. Leary; preface by Wayne
Franklin.—1st ed.
    p. cm.—(The American land and
life series)
ISBN 0-87745-278-4 (alk. paper)
1. Air-pilot guides—United States.
2. Air mail service—United
States—History. I. Leary, William
M. (William Matthew), 1934–
II. Series.
TL726.2.P53   1990   89-20479
629.132'5473—dc20   CIP

CONTENTS

PREFACE

BY WAYNE FRANKLIN

Despite its utterly pragmatic purpose and title, the United States Post Office's *Pilots' Directions* of 1921 offers something more than practical counsel for would-be airmail pilots. It also provides an intriguing vision of how America looked from a largely new— and wonderfully revealing—perspective some seventy years ago. This seemingly modest little guidebook is crammed with incidental revelations that crop up throughout like a line of trees jutting in front of a low-flying de Havilland biplane. It guided pilots by mapping in sharp detail a cross section of the land over which they picked their way at no great altitude, from field to field, from crash to crash, through headwinds, bad rain, and blinding snow. Since the purpose of the book was to help pilots keep their senses in such conditions, it reads today like an infinite series of landscape photos. It shows us how the cultural designs of the United States had been inscribed on the clean slate of a continent that in 1921 had, over all its vast distances, a dominantly rural note.

By now we are so accustomed to what have become the clichés of aerial imagery that we may forget how startling the first aerial vision of this continent must have been. Although imaginary views and balloonists' photographs provided a rudimentary glimpse of America from above long before the Wright brothers, most Americans before 1900 thought of their land pretty much as they saw it in their daily circuits over its surface. When they looked around, they saw an immediate collection of objects impinging on their senses. The patterns which made those objects cohere, which made *landscape* as the pilot sees it, could not emerge easily from an earthbound perspective. The machine which conquered the land was also to give ordinary citizens a dramatic new appreciation for its beauty. As if in preparation for this revealing new view, the patterns on the land itself were taking on a more nearly rational shape in the century before the Wrights. It was as if the land was being constructed to make its order more readily intelligible from the air. Generally speaking, American land east of the Appalachians had been subdivided and settled in earlier centuries according to local topographic conditions and the needs of the local populace. Along a line that roughly follows the Ohio River until turning south through Kentucky and Tennessee and then passing on toward the Gulf Coast, there is a strong contrast between the aerial crazy quilt of the East, produced by this traditional approach, and the stark symmetry of the newer national grid of the Midwest and the West. The mile-square sections of this grid were surveyed before settlement to aid government and settler alike in locating particular tracts. Their corners marked by posts or rock piles, the sections had only the faintest physical presence on the land at the start. Soon, however, farmers enclosed their sections or quarter sections (640 or 160 acres) with fences, giving the faint legal lines an indelible, three-dimensional inscription. Local roads ran as straight as a bee's flight, mile by mile, along the government's abstract gridwork. The fences gave the mathematical system imagined by Thomas Jefferson in the 1780s an agrarian actuality as real as stone, wood, and wire.

The pilots who scouted out the Post Office route of 1921 found the human landscape east of Cleveland haphazardly scrawled on the face of nature. Here space was largely pre-Jeffersonian in design. Hence the *Directions* comments on the exceptional linearity of one part of New Jersey where three features—"mountain, railroad, and river"—run parallel to each other. Hence, too, the similar comment about one area of middle Pennsylvania, where "Bigler, Bradford, and Clearfield cemeteries all [lie] in [a] direct line." More typically eastern is the lack of large articulated patterns anywhere on the land. When acreages in the East are given, they tend to be in odd amounts, and the dimensions of emergency landing fields there are also likely to be irregular. As glimpsed in this pilots' guidebook, the East remains a landscape of often unrationalized fragments, with no overarching system. (One emergency field in Pennsylvania is stated to be 1,075 feet long and 370 feet wide. By comparison, a field in Nebraska is described as a mile long and a quarter mile wide, a mark of the grid's great regularizing rhythms.)

Anywhere in America at this time, east or west, pilots would inch along over a land that hardly acknowledged their needs or even their very presence above. Beneath them, indeterminate and ambiguous, lay a world organized laterally rather than vertically, a world which for all its beauty from this new vantage point was damned hard to read. It was decidedly not what one might call a pilot-friendly landscape. Airports were meager enough, there were no radio beacons, and if one lost one's way—or one's airspeed—the land might prove as frighteningly alien as the surface of Mars. Pilots often simply didn't know where they were. Only a few communities had as yet painted their names on the roof of some convenient structure, an act which would make the landscape immensely more legible. An occasional athletic team's signet on a western hillside (as in the case of Laramie's W of whitewashed stones), though not intended for pilots, also gave some textual order to the flow of impressions below.

Amid all this confusion, the gridwork of the nation's midsection and far west gave some additional comfort. Hence, "by keeping on the section lines and flying directly west," the pilots could find their way across Illinois, over the Mississippi, and into Iowa. In Nebraska, section lines had been inscribed so accurately that pilots could use them to determine the correct compass bearing for North Platte and even Cheyenne. At one point pilots are instructed to drop south one section for every twenty-five that they fly west in Nebraska, until they arrive over Central City, from which point the section lines would lead "directly into North Platte." It is as if the technological exactitude which underpinned the invention of powered flight and the mathematical precision of Jefferson's land system were converging here. Jefferson's West was a more navigable landscape than the old territories of the East. Surveyors had prepared a continent for the machines which engineers would come to build more than a century later.

But it will not do to stress too strongly this difference between the East and the West in the pilot's experience during the early decades. From a pilot's vantage point, as I have said, the United States at this time was a largely oblivious, often dangerous blur of space against which, at any moment, one might come crashing down. Some of the emergency landing fields, barely visible from the air and encumbered with all kinds of dangerous impediments—coal diggings, irrigation ditches, power lines, houses, stones, drainageways, garden patches, fences, cattle, mud, high trees, telephone poles, hills, sagebrush—must have offered scant comfort to a pilot in trouble. Putting a plane down in a 400-foot-wide evaporation vat in the Utah desert hardly strikes me as a way *out* of danger: to land in such an emergency field was itself a sizable emergency. I shudder in reading that the "only field suitable for landing planes" in Rockland, Pennsylvania, was "5 acres in [the] school yard."

The nation as the pilots of the 1920s knew it cohered from the air not as it does today—not via an elaborate structure of visible and invisible navigational and guidance systems but rather by haphazard and discontinuous means. Very few major highways went for even modest distances along rational routings, so few that they are very rarely mentioned in the guidebook. Only the railroads, the nation's first great infrastructure, were seen from the sky easily enough and often enough to lend a kind of continuous aid. Again and again the guidebook leads pilots over the landscape by means of the steel tracks and wooden sleepers which in 1921 knit the nation together.

There was something ominous in this alliance of train and plane. The airplane in these years was a frail competitor for the railroad, despite the heroic pilots of whom William Leary writes in his introduction. Yet the airplane would come (along with the car) to turn many of those shining steel rails on the land rusty with disuse. By following the tracks, the airmail pilots were helping to erase them from a landscape where they had only recently been inscribed. That effacement was to be a long time in coming, but its inevitability should remind us that the airplane's purchase on the continent, feeble as it was then, was to get stronger with every year. In 1921, the bulk of America's mail went by train, in special cars where it was sorted en route. In 1990, none of it is moved by train, but vast quantities crisscross the sky above us, following invisible air routes pioneered decades ago.

INTRODUCTION

BY WILLIAM M. LEARY

The first generation of pilots made up an intrepid breed. From the beginning, they tested the limits of the new technology, constantly pushing the "outside of the envelope" in their frail, underpowered machines. In September 1908, Wilbur and Orville Wright amazed the world by staying aloft for more than one hour, setting new endurance records. The following year, on July 25, Louis Blériot created an even greater sensation when he became the first person to fly across the English Channel.[1]

A sense of adventure animated these early birdmen as they competed for the lucrative prizes offered by newspapers and by the organizers of aviation meets. Blériot received one thousand pounds from the *London Daily Mail* for his twenty-mile adventure. In May 1910, Glenn Curtiss collected ten thousand dollars from the *New York World* when he flew the 135 miles between Albany and New York City. William Randolph Hearst, the flamboyant newspaper magnate, offered the largest prize of all: fifty thousand dollars to the first pilot to span the continent. The flight could take no more than thirty days, and it had to be completed by October 10, 1911.

At a time when the average American worker earned less than a thousand dollars a year, the Hearst prize amounted to a small fortune. But Hearst's money seemed safe, as the transcontinental voyage appeared far beyond the capabilities of

---

1. On the first aviators, see Henry Serrano Villard, *Contact! The Story of the Early Birds* (New York, 1968).

existing aircraft. Nevertheless, in September 1911, shortly before the offer lapsed, Calbraith Perry Rodgers accepted the
challenge and set out to cross the country by air.[2]

Descended from Captain Oliver Hazard Perry, hero of the
Battle of Lake Erie in the War of 1812, and Commodore
Matthew Calbraith Perry, who opened Japan to the West in
the 1850s, the six-foot-four, cigar-smoking motorcycle en-
thusiast shared the intrepid spirit of his ancestors. A novice
aviator, with only sixty hours in his logbook, Rodgers had se-
cured the backing of the Armour Meat Packing Company of
Chicago. Anxious to promote a new carbonated grape drink
named Vin Fiz, Armour agreed to pay Rodgers five dollars for
every mile flown east of the Mississippi and four dollars for
every mile west of the river. The company also supplied a five-
car special train to trail the aviator, carrying mechanics, reporters, a disassembled second airplane, spare parts, and Mrs.
Rodgers. In return, Rodgers would display the name and logo
of the soft drink on his airplane and toss out promotional leaf-
lets en route.

Rodgers departed Sheepshead Bay, New York, on September 17, flying a Wright Model Ex. This state-of-the-art machine was a modified version of the famous Wright Model B.
Powered by a four-cylinder, thirty-five-horsepower, water-
cooled engine, it was capable of a top speed of fifty-five miles
an hour. Lacking navigational instruments, including a compass, Rodgers planned to follow the railroad tracks to California. He would head westward to Chicago, then swing south
to Texas. In order to avoid mountainous terrain, he would
cross over the deserts of southern New Mexico, Arizona, and
California.

Rodgers hoped to reach Chicago in four days. It took twenty-
one days—and three major crashes—to cover the 750 miles.

2. Eileen F. Lebow, *Cal Rodgers and the Vin Fiz: The First Transcontinental Flight* (Washington, D.C., 1989), is the best book on the subject.

INTRODUCTION

Although it now was obvious that he could not complete the journey before the Hearst prize expired, Rodgers decided to press on. "I am bound for Los Angeles and the Pacific Ocean," he told reporters. "Prize or no prize, that's where I am bound, and if canvas, steel, and wire together with a little brawn, tendon, and brain stick with me, I mean to get there."

Day after day, mile after mile, crash after crash, the determined aviator pressed westward. By October 10, the day the Hearst offer lapsed, he had reached Marshall, Missouri, setting a new cross-country record of 1,398 miles. It took another three weeks to reach Tucson. On November 3, as he neared the end of his journey, Rodgers nearly came to grief when his engine exploded over the Salton Sea, sending metal shards into his right arm. Rodgers managed to land safely. The next day, after a doctor had removed the metal splinters and mechanics had changed the engine, he resumed his transcontinental odyssey.

Finally, on Sunday, November 5, Rodgers landed in Tournament Park, Pasadena, California. It had taken him forty-nine days to cover the 4,231 miles. He had survived fifteen major accidents. Of the original airplane, only the rudder and drip pan from the engine remained.

Most men would have been satisfied with this impressive accomplishment, but not Rodgers. He did not consider his trip finished until he had dipped his landing gear into the Pacific Ocean. On November 6, he left Pasadena for Long Beach. Halfway to his final destination, a control wire broke, and Rodgers once again crashed to the ground. This time his injuries were serious: a concussion, two broken legs, several cracked ribs, and assorted burns and bruises.

Rodgers spent a month convalescing from his injuries. On December 10, eighty-four days after he had left New York, the stubborn pilot lashed his crutches behind the seat of his battered airplane and flew to Long Beach. Interviewed by the press, Rodgers predicted rapid advances in aeronautics. He expected to see the day, he said, when airplanes would carry passengers from coast to coast at speeds of one hundred miles an hour.

That day would come, but Rodgers would not be around to see it. On April 3, 1912, while making an exhibition flight at Long Beach, he crashed into the ocean and was killed.

Eight years after Rodgers's epic of endurance, public interest once again focused on a coast-to-coast spectacular. In September 1919, the U.S. Army Air Service announced that it would conduct a "transcontinental reliability test." This prosaic description failed to mask the true nature of the event. As the *New York Times* pointed out, the American people were about to witness "the greatest air race ever attempted."[3]

The main reason for the contest, an Air Service spokesman announced, was to demonstrate the great advances in aeronautical technology that had taken place during the recent war. Aeronautics could now be put to peaceful purposes. Surely, a well-organized transcontinental air route would be of enormous commercial value. "As a result of this race," Lt. Col. Horace M. Hickam emphasized, "we will have such a route in a practicable, workable condition. It seems to me that the importance of this to commercial aviation cannot be overestimated."

Beyond the stated purpose for the race lay the desire of airpower enthusiasts, led by Brig. Gen. William "Billy" Mitchell, to mobilize public opinion in support of their proposal for an independent air force. Congress had before it a bill for a separate air service, but legislators seemed more concerned with cutting funds for military aviation than creating a new air force. Mitchell and his associates believed that this trend could be reversed only by focusing the pressure of public opinion on the issue.

3. See Ray L. Bowers, "The Transcontinental Reliability Test," *Airpower Historian* 8 (January 1961): 45–54; (April 1961): 88–100.

INTRODUCTION

In preparation for the race, the Air Service laid out a 2,701-mile route from New York to San Francisco, with twenty intermediate landing points that included Buffalo, Cleveland, Chicago, Omaha, Cheyenne, Salt Lake City, Reno, and Sacramento. Airmen would follow the tracks of railroads as they crossed the country. The railroad route offered the same compelling advantages in 1919 that it had for Cal Rodgers in 1911: it followed favorable terrain, supplies and equipment could easily be moved by rail to intermediate fields, and the tracks would serve as the primary navigational aid for crossing the country, especially from Omaha to San Francisco.

The great transcontinental air race got under way on October 8, 1919, with forty-eight airplanes starting from New York and fifteen from San Francisco. Everything began well enough. On the East Coast, more than two thousand people showed up at Roosevelt Field, Long Island, to cheer the fliers on their way. The 22nd Infantry Band provided music, while women from the War Camp Community Service passed out sandwiches and coffee. Assistant Secretary of War Benedict Crowell, in a short speech, voiced his hope that the race would cause the American people "to take aviation seriously in national defense and commerce. America should lead the world in aviation." Billy Mitchell then gave the signal to start the race. Lt. J. B. Machle was first off the ground at 9:13 A.M. The other aviators quickly followed.

Secretary Crowell, caught up in the spirit of things, decided that he wanted an airplane ride. Mitchell made the necessary arrangements, borrowing goggles and a leather jacket for the enthusiastic bureaucrat. Crowell waved to the crowd as he climbed into the back seat of a Curtiss biplane, piloted by Capt. M. G. Cleary. Cleary taxied to the edge of the field, turned into the wind, and began to take off. Just as his wheels left the ground, Cleary's engine failed. The Curtiss stalled to the right, a wingtip hit the ground, and the airplane flipped over onto its back. Crowell and Cleary emerged from the wreck shaken but uninjured. "That's the shortest flight on record," Crowell quipped to reporters. The secretary said that he was ready to go up again; unfortunately, a "pressing appointment" in the city prevented another flight.

As it turned out, Crowell's near disaster set the tone for the first day of the race. Commodore L. E. O. Charlton, the British air attaché who was participating as a courtesy, wrecked his Bristol fighter during an emergency landing in upstate New York. Lt. D. G. Gish narrowly escaped death when his aircraft caught fire over Livingston, New York. Sgt. W. H. Nevitt was not as fortunate. A passenger with Col. Joseph Brant, he was killed during an emergency landing at Deposit, New York.

Meanwhile, the smaller group of eastbound fliers had managed to cross the treacherous Sierra Nevadas without incident. But their luck ran out at Salt Lake City. Major Dana Crissey and Sgt. Virgil Thomas arrived over the city in late afternoon. Everything appeared normal as they circled the airfield prior to landing. On final approach, however, the aircraft stalled and smashed into the ground, killing both occupants.

The next day, October 9, brought little relief for the dwindling number of transcontinental racers. Rainstorms east of the Mississippi caused numerous forced landings and four major accidents. In the west, Lts. E. V. Wales and William Goldsborough crashed into the side of a mountain during a snowstorm. Wales was killed, and Goldsborough suffered serious injuries.

The third day saw three major accidents and another death. Major A. L. Sneed made an especially hard landing at Buffalo. The aircraft bounced into the air, then smacked down onto its nose. Sgt. Worth C. McClure, sitting in the back seat, was pitched out and broke his neck.

The first phase of the race ended on October 11, without additional fatalities. Lt. Belvin W. Maynard, a teetotaling part-time preacher, was the first westbound flier to reach San Francisco, arriving in early afternoon. His flying time of 24:59

set a new transcontinental speed record. A few hours later, Lt. Emil Kiel led the eastbound racers into New York.

Sunday, October 12, a mandatory day of rest for the tired aviators, gave Billy Mitchell and his supporters a chance to end a public relations effort that had backfired. With newspapers across the country criticizing the high human cost of the race and several pilots threatening to abandon the wreck-strewn course, the Air Service should have found some face-saving way to end the transcontinental fiasco. But military discipline prevailed: the Air Service ordered the race to continue.

Resumption of flying brought a resumption of fatalities. On October 15, Lts. French Kirby and Stanley C. Miller were killed near Evanston, Wyoming, while trying to make an emergency landing in a blizzard. This brought the death toll to seven, equaling the number of Americans killed in twenty-two months of combat while flying with the Lafayette Escadrille.

Three days later, Lieutenant Maynard—labeled the "Flying Preacher" by the press—landed at Roosevelt Field and claimed victory in the air race. Seven other pilots went on to complete the round-trip crossing of the country before the Air Service declared the contest over at sundown on October 31. Although accidents continued until the end, there were no additional fatalities.

Mitchell's attempt to focus public opinion on aviation had worked, but not in the way he had intended. Instead of showcasing advances in aviation, the air race had demonstrated that unreliable engines, inadequate navigational instruments, and primitive landing facilities were commonplace. Mitchell failed to secure an increase in appropriations for the Air Service, and unification remained a dream.

The race also had an adverse impact on plans by the Post Office to operate a transcontinental airmail service. Postal officials had hoped that the contest would generate favorable publicity and persuade Congress to fund a transcontinental route. This now seemed unlikely. Taking the accident figures from the race, the *New York Sun* calculated that a coast-to-coast mail service would cost the lives of three or four pilots a month. Such an operation, it argued, would not be progress; "in light of what happened in the recent race, it is more like homicidal insanity."

Otto Praeger, the postal official in charge of the government's Air Mail Service, disagreed with the *Sun*'s gloomy assessment. Speaking before the American Flying Club in New York City, Praeger declared that the air race *had* demonstrated the practicality of transcontinental airmail service. "We can and will extend the air post to San Francisco by next Spring," he told the audience; Congress, however, would have to provide the necessary funds.[4]

If determination could accomplish the objective of coast-to-coast airmail service, Praeger surely had that quality in full measure. The son of a German immigrant to Texas, he had grown up in the large German-American community in the San Antonio area. After high school, Praeger went to work for a local newspaper. Eventually, he became the Washington correspondent for the influential *Dallas News*.

In April 1914, Postmaster General Albert S. Burleson resolved a patronage dispute with Secretary of State William Jennings Bryan by appointing Praeger—an old fishing and hunting buddy—as postmaster of Washington, D.C. The newspaperman proved a highly competent administrator, directing the modernization of the city's antiquated postal system. Among other innovations, Praeger introduced a government-operated automotive mail delivery system, replacing the horse-drawn vehicles of private contractors. A delighted Burleson in September 1915 promoted Praeger to second assistant post-

4. William M. Leary, *Aerial Pioneers: The U.S. Air Mail Service, 1918–1927* (Washington, D.C., 1985), details the work of Otto Praeger and the Post Office's airmail operations.

master general, in charge of all mail transportation in the United States.

Looking for new ways to advance the mails, Praeger soon became interested in the possibilities of an airmail service. At first, he attempted to contract with responsible private companies to operate an experimental service. Although enthusiastic promoters were full of schemes for airmail routes, regular aerial operations proved beyond their technical competence. Praeger eventually decided that the Post Office would have to do the job with its own planes and pilots. In February 1918, he called for bids to construct five airplanes for a Washington–New York mail route. However, just as the bids were about to be unsealed, the Army Air Service stepped in and volunteered to operate the route with military airplanes and pilots.

The country's first regularly scheduled airmail service opened with great fanfare on May 15, 1918. Even President Woodrow Wilson took time off from his demanding wartime responsibilities to attend the inaugural. At 11:46 A.M., Lt. George L. Boyle departed Washington's Polo Field with 140 pounds of mail for Philadelphia and New York. Unfortunately, the young pilot became lost en route when he followed the wrong railroad tracks out of Washington. Attempting to land to get directions, Boyle managed to nose over, flipping the Jenny on its back. To Praeger's great chagrin, the mail went by train.

Although operational efficiency improved in the weeks ahead, Praeger remained dissatisfied with the army's performance. All too often, in his view, the military pilots canceled flights for no good reason. He had promised Burleson that the airmail would become a dependable part of postal operations. Intolerant of the technological limitations that prevented daily scheduled service, Praeger decided that only greater control by the Post Office would bring about the necessary regularity. Burleson agreed. On August 12, 1918, the War Department relinquished operation of the airmail to the Post Office. Praeger would operate the route with his own planes and pilots.

Over the next fifteen months, the Post Office's Air Mail Service compiled a remarkable record. Praeger pushed aeronautical technology to the limit, demanding a level of performance from his pilots that was without equal in the world. Despite balky engines, primitive instruments, and treacherous landing fields, the courageous postal pilots flew through snow, fog, and thunderstorms to deliver the mail on time.

From the beginning, Praeger had in mind a network of airmail routes, radiating out from a transcontinental trunk line. In December 1918, he tried to open a New York–Chicago route, but bad weather and equipment shortages forced him to abandon it within a week. The following May, however, the Chicago–Cleveland portion of the route reopened, followed by the Cleveland–New York segment in July.

Praeger had expected Billy Mitchell's transcontinental extravaganza to pave the way for a sympathetic congressional reception to the Post Office's request for funds to operate a coast-to-coast airmail route. But Congress, controlled by the Republican party since the election of 1918, proved no friendlier to the Post Office than it had to the Air Service. In December 1919, Praeger asked the House Post Office Committee to approve $3 million for the Air Mail Service, including $1 million to extend the New York–Chicago route to San Francisco. The committee, however, voted not to increase appropriations beyond the $850,000 necessary to operate the Washington–New York route. Moreover, during consideration of the postal appropriation bill on the floor of the House, all funding for the airmail was stricken from the bill on a point-of-order.

Praeger turned to the more sympathetic Senate for support. Testifying before the Senate Post Office Committee, he argued that the mail could be carried from coast to coast by air in fifty-six to fifty-nine hours by daylight and in thirty-six to forty hours when night flying was introduced. This compared to ninety to 102 hours by the fastest rail connections. Furthermore, Praeger claimed that the mail could be transported by air for less than what it cost by rail. According to his optimistic figures, it would take $1,043,363 to operate the airmail route from New York to San Francisco for one year. When car space, distribution, clerical, and other expenses were taken into account, it would cost $1,222,803 to move the same amount of mail by train.

While even the most friendly legislators likely discounted Praeger's unrealistic economic projections, the Senate did approve the funds necessary to operate the transcontinental route. The House-Senate conference committee accepted the Senate's version of the postal appropriations bill, which both houses then adopted without debate.

Praeger now had the necessary fiscal mandate for the transcontinental airmail. Two tasks lay ahead. He had to locate suitable airports for the route west of Chicago, and he had to acquire suitable aircraft.

Finding airports was no easy task. Under existing law, the Post Office could not use federal funds to pay for airports. Instead, local officials had to be persuaded that construction of airfields was in their best interest. In order to sell local communities on the idea, Praeger sent John A. Jordan as his special representative to cities west of Chicago.

Jordan was a bit of a snake-oil salesman. In May 1920, he visited Cheyenne, met with the chamber of commerce, and outlined plans for the transcontinental mail. Cheyenne, he pointed out, would have to raise money to clear a field and erect a hangar. The Post Office, he stressed, wanted to stop at Cheyenne, which would surely benefit from its position as a terminus on the air route. In all fairness, however, Jordan had to point out that discussions were also taking place with people from Laramie. Indeed, Laramie was anxious to provide the necessary facilities. The city of Cheyenne promptly appropriated fifteen thousand dollars for the privilege of becoming an airmail station.

Jordan made the same sales pitch in Reno, this time using Carson City to frighten the town's leaders. Reno quickly fell in line to the tune of twenty-nine thousand dollars. Salt Lake City came next. After listening to Jordan's blandishments, the city appropriated twenty-seven thousand dollars for an airfield and hangar lest Odgen make a deal with the Post Office and reap the economic benefits and prestige that were rightfully Salt Lake City's!

Although Jordan's tactics later became the subject of a congressional inquiry, at the time they worked beautifully. By September, Praeger had the necessary ground facilities for the transcontinental service.

Locating first-rate equipment turned out to be more difficult. The Post Office operated the New York–Washington and New York–Chicago routes primarily with de Havilland DH-4s. Based on a British design and powered by a four-hundred-horsepower Liberty engine, these American-built biplanes had given reliable service, at least after an initial teething period. Praeger, however, wanted an airplane that could carry a greater load than the DH's two hundred to three hundred pounds, at a higher speed, and over longer distances.

For a time, the answer to the Post Office's problem seemed to be solved with the appearance of a twin-DH. Working with eighteen thousand dollars of Post Office funds, the L.W.F. Engineering Company used parts from surplus DHs to build a twin-engine aircraft that could fly faster and carry twice the load of the standard DH. Following initial tests, an ecstatic Praeger hailed the twin-DH as "the single greatest contribution during the year, commercially as well as mechanically, of the Air Mail Service to commercial aviation." He promptly ordered fifteen standard DHs converted to twin-DHs at the bargain price of only seven thousand dollars per airplane.

Unfortunately, the marvelous machine soon ran into troubled times. Shortly after being placed into service on the New York–Chicago route, the twin-DHs began to fall out of the sky. Pilot Walter Stevens, en route from Chicago to Cleveland on August 11, started a turn when he felt something snap on the right side of the aircraft. The twin-DH whipped over to the right and dove into the ground. Stevens survived but the aircraft was demolished. A few days later, pilot Oscar B. Santa-Maria was cruising at two thousand feet in a twin-DH when something gave way. The left engine began to vibrate, the left wing dropped, and the aircraft spiraled into the ground. Again, the pilot escaped serious injury. In the wake of the two accidents, plus other reports by pilots of excessive vibration and poor performance, Praeger had no choice except to withdraw the planes from service.

The failure of the twin-DHs was not as painful as it might have been, because the Post Office had already found an even better airplane for the transcontinental service. In May 1920, as Jordan began his westward swing in search of airports, John M. Larsen was touting the advantages of a new airplane that he had imported from Germany. Designed by Hugo Junkers, the F.13 was far ahead of its time, both in structure and in aeronautical design. In place of the externally braced wings of traditional biplanes, Junkers had come up with a cantilever (internally braced) monoplane that had a duraluminum (metal) structure covered with corrugated dural skin instead of fabric. The F.13 featured a semi-enclosed cockpit with dual controls and an enclosed cabin that could seat four passengers. Powered by a single 185-horsepower B.M.W. IIIa six-cylinder, water-cooled, in-line engine, it had a slower cruising speed (eighty miles an hour) than a DH, but it could carry twice the load over three times the distance. Larsen, a former munitions dealer, had purchased the American rights to the F.13. He planned to import several planes from Germany, then manufacture them in the United States under the designation JL-6.

INTRODUCTION

Word of the unique airplane quickly spread, and the U.S. Army and Navy promptly purchased six of the metal machines. The Post Office also expressed interest. With the beginning of the fiscal year in sight (July 1), Praeger had enough money to strike a deal with Larsen. For the bargain price of $200,000, the Air Mail Service acquired eight JL-6s and a long list of spares. Praeger planned to use them on the eastern half of the transcontinental route. If they proved satisfactory, he would shift them to the west in order to take advantage of the greater altitude capability of their high-compression B.M.W. engines.

As plans for transcontinental service neared completion, Larsen, the Army Air Service, and the Post Office collaborated on a survey flight of the route. Three JL-6s left New York on July 29, bound for the West Coast. They made a leisurely tour of eastern airmail fields, stopped at Chicago, then flew on to Omaha. On August 3, in hot weather, two aircraft took off from Omaha without incident. The third, flown by Lt. Col. H. H. Hartney, with wartime ace Edward V. Rickenbacker as passenger, barely got off the ground before striking an empty house at the end of the runway. The plane hit the ground, suffering major damage. Hartney was uninjured, and Rickenbacker came away with only a slight bruise on the head. ("I suffered a severe fracture of the straw hat," Rickenbacker told reporters.) The other two planes returned to Omaha, picked up Rickenbacker, and resumed their westward journey. After stopping at North Platte, Cheyenne, Salt Lake City, Elko, and Reno, they reached San Francisco without further incident, arriving on August 8. One aircraft remained on the West Coast while the other returned to New York by a circuitous southern route, completing the round trip on August 22.

The transcontinental survey, despite the incident at Omaha (which was blamed on the hot day and short field), seemed to bode well for the coast-to-coast airmail. "Our journey was as safe as if made in a Pullman," Rickenbacker boasted. "It proves—if proof is needed—the wonderful worth and reliability of the JL-6." *Aerial Age Weekly* agreed, hailing the trip as "one of the most remarkable performances in the history of flying."

The postal JL-6s went into service in late August, with transcontinental operations scheduled to begin in early September. Pilots soon reported problems with the aircraft due to excessive vibration, radiator leaks, fuel leaks, and clogged fuel strainers. Still, these kinds of difficulties were not too surprising with a new aircraft, and the Post Office expected to have all the defects fixed within a short time.

On August 31, Wesley L. Smith was en route from Chicago to Cleveland with a Junkers, flying at eight thousand feet in clear weather, when a fuel leak developed. As it did not seem serious, he decided to continue to Cleveland. Just south of Toledo, however, the engine quit. Thinking that a tank had run dry, Smith was in the process of switching tanks when his feet were engulfed in flames that had burned through the metal floor of the cockpit. He turned off the fuel and put the airplane into a vertical sideslip to the right, away from the flames. The aircraft became uncontrollable for a time, but Smith managed to put it into a flat glide as he neared the ground. Spotting a cornfield, he stalled the airplane on top of the six-foot-high stalks. Thanks to his leather helmet, long leather coat, and puttees, Smith escaped with only nasty facial burns.

The next day, while officials tried to sort out the reason for Smith's accident, pilot Max Miller and mechanic Gustav Reierson left New York for Cleveland in a JL-6 with six hundred pounds of mail. Two hours after departure, the Junkers was spotted over Morristown, New Jersey—inexplicably, only twenty miles from its point of departure—flying low and with its motor cutting out and backfiring. Within minutes, flames billowed out, engulfing the entire front end of the aircraft.

INTRODUCTION

The JL-6 nosed over, dove into the ground, and exploded. Fire consumed the fuselage until it collapsed into a broken heap of metal, a pyre for the bodies of Miller and Reierson. Praeger ordered the Junkers grounded following the deaths of Miller and Reierson. At the same time, he insisted that the inauguration of transcontinental service go forward on schedule. For the time being, at least, DH-4s would be used on the route.

Only a small crowd turned out on September 8, 1920, to cheer Randolph G. Page as he left New York on the first leg of the transcontinental service. Philatelists showed more enthusiasm, providing most of the sixteen thousand letters for the flight. When the mail load proved too great to fit into the forward mail compartment of the DH, Page ordered the extra letters placed into a suitcase that was strapped to the lower wing of the aircraft. After this brief delay, he took off at 6:41 A.M.

The mail traveled westward in relays. Page stopped at Bellefonte, Cleveland, and Chicago, where a new plane and pilot took over. James P. Murray hoped to reach Omaha before dark, but this proved impossible, and he had to land at Iowa City. Murray left Iowa City at 10:15 A.M. the next day. It took most of the remaining daylight to cover the 686 miles to Cheyenne, including stops at Omaha and North Platte. The transcontinental schedule called for the mail to arrive in San Francisco in the early evening of the third day. Delays on the final portion of the trip, however, prevented a timely arrival on the West Coast. It was not until 2:33 P.M., September 11, that Edison E. Mouton touched down at Marina Field, near the Presidio, and completed the first scheduled transcontinental mail service.

Although the Post Office's schedule called for a coast-to-coast transit in fifty-four hours, the first trip had taken nearly eighty-three. Nonetheless, it was an impressive achievement. "The mail fliers of 1920," the *Literary Digest* proclaimed, "are following the intrepid example of the couriers of Revolu-

tionary times, the Pony Express riders, the frontier telegraph
linesmen, and the railroad builders. They are worthy successors." Mrs. Alice Hunt Bartlett, noted more for her civic activities than her poetry, celebrated the Post Office's triumph
in verse:

> A rousing cheer from coast to coast resounds
> To you, swift couriers, controlling flight!
> Nor sun, nor rain, nor heat, nor gloom of night
> Shall stay you from completion of your rounds.
> To you! The big planes ride our skies each day—
> Transcontinental Air Mail: here to stay!

Anxious to maintain the transcontinental schedule, Praeger
pressed for return to service of the JL-6s. When inspections
by the maintenance department failed to reveal any problems
with the aircraft, they were again placed on the New York–
Omaha route. This proved a tragic mistake.

On September 14, pilot Walter Stevens and mechanic
Russell Thomas were flying between Cleveland and Toledo in
JL-6 no. 308. As the airplane neared Pemberville, Ohio, ob-
servers on the ground heard its engine cutting in and out.
Suddenly, it burst into flames. The Junkers continued level for
about a half mile, then plunged into a clover field at a 45-
degree angle and blew up. The largest remaining piece of the
airplane measured three feet by eight feet.

Once again, the Junkers were grounded. This time a more
thorough investigation revealed that a defective fuel system
had caused the accidents. The JL-6 burned antidetonation
benzol that had to be piped through rigid lines and connections because it would burn through rubber. The engine vi-
brated badly, causing fuel leaks. As no provision had been
made for the leaking benzol to escape, fuel and fumes collected beneath the engine. Fuel starvation caused the engine
to backfire, exploding the benzol that had accumulated in the
engine compartment.

Even without the Junkers in service, the transcontinental

service continued to suffer losses. On September 27, Frederick Robinson, flying low in bad weather, struck heavy cables that spanned the Susquehanna River at Millersburg, Pennsylvania. The DH slammed into the riverbank, killing Robinson. Two weeks later, Bryan McMullen stalled his DH while trying to squeeze into a small field near Batavia, Illinois, in bad weather. The airplane spun into the ground and exploded, killing McMullen.

The Post Office came under heavy attack in the press. The unfriendly *New York Sun* labeled the transcontinental service "Burleson's Deadly Fad" and noted that its earlier prediction of heavy losses was coming true. Even newspapers that had long supported the airmail began to register doubts. The *New York Times*, for example, hailed as "remarkable" the work being done by the Post Office in developing long-distance airmail routes, but added that "success at an unnecessary cost of life would be deplorable."

A deteriorating political situation during the winter of 1920–21 added to the Post Office woes. Warren G. Harding's victory in November (he would be inaugurated in March) meant that Burleson and Praeger were members of an outgoing administration. They would have to go to Congress for money that their Republican successors would spend. Furthermore, it was clear that economy would be the keynote of the new administration.

Praeger sounded the new theme of economy when he asked the House for $3,500,000 to carry airmail during the fiscal year beginning July 1, 1921. Although members of the House Appropriations Committee were not persuaded by Praeger's figures (according to their calculations, it cost $5.38 a ton-mile to carry mail by air versus seven cents a ton-mile by rail), they voted $1,250,000 to continue the coast-to-coast service as an experiment. However, even this modest sum fell victim to a point-of-order on the floor of the House.

Praeger again turned to the Senate to save the Air Mail Service. In his search for continued funding, he received strong support from the influential National Advisory Committee for Aeronautics, the government's expert body on aviation. "The Air Mail Service," it argued, "has given the best demonstration of the practicality of the use of aircraft for civil purposes and, in the face of many obstacles, has accomplished remarkable results of real and permanent value to the Nation at relatively slight cost." The committee urged Congress to continue this "experimental laboratory" for the development of commercial aviation.

The Senate, as usual, came to the rescue of the Air Mail Service. On January 25, the Post Office Committee approved $1,500,000 for the airmail. However, unlike the previous year, postal officials realized that the House could not be counted on to go along with even this modest appropriation. In order to mobilize support for the airmail, and at the same time demonstrate the potential of the transcontinental service, Praeger ordered the mail carried from coast to coast by day *and* by night.

Praeger once more was calling upon his pilots to test the limits of aeronautical technology. Before the war, only exhibition pilots, intent upon thrilling their audiences, had done any nighttime flying. Later, the British had launched a limited number of wartime night bombing missions, considered an extremely hazardous undertaking. But at a time when pilots needed to see the ground in order to navigate from point to point, nowhere in the world had scheduled nighttime flying operations been attempted.

The Post Office's record-breaking effort got under way on February 22 when two airplanes started out on the East Coast and two on the West Coast, each carrying 350 pounds of mail. Their schedule called for the transcontinental run to be made in thirty-six hours or less. The westbound planes, flying into bad weather east of the Mississippi River, soon ran into trouble. They flew from New York to Bellefonte without incident, but ice forced one plane down en route to Cleveland. Although the second DH managed to reach Chicago, a combination of rain, snow, and fog made it impossible to continue. If Praeger's dramatic demonstration was not to fall flat, the eastbound mail would have to make it through.

Farr Nutter and Raymond J. Little departed San Francisco at 4:30 A.M. (All times are local.) Flying mostly in darkness, they crossed the Sierra Nevadas at altitudes that reached eighteen thousand feet and landed at Reno before 7 A.M. It took only ten minutes for the mail to be transferred to waiting airplanes. Samuel C. Eaton and William F. Lewis flew to Elko in good weather, where they changed planes for the next leg to Salt Lake City. Eaton took off without incident, but Lewis stalled his DH when five hundred feet off the ground, crashed, and was killed. His mail, which had escaped damage, was loaded onto another airplane, which departed shortly before noon.

Eaton flew the 204 miles from Elko to Salt Lake City in two hours. There, James P. Murray loaded the eastbound mail and headed across the rugged Wasatch Range for Cheyenne. After landing at Rawlins for oil, he reached his destination at 4:57 P.M. Meanwhile, William F. Blanchfield had reached Salt Lake City. Topcliffe Paine then carried the mail to Cheyenne via a refueling stop at Rock Springs, arriving one hour after Murray.

Frank R. Yager flew Murray's mail to North Platte, landing in darkness at 7:48 P.M. Jack Knight was waiting to take the mail to Omaha, but Yager's DH had developed ignition trouble and no spare aircraft had been allotted for this leg of the trip. While mechanics tried to correct the faulty ignition, Harry G. Smith arrived from Cheyenne. At 9:20 P.M., following a thirty-four-minute stop for servicing, Smith continued on to Omaha. Knight, his mechanical difficulty remedied, followed one hour later.

Smith and Knight flew the 248 miles from North Platte to Omaha in deteriorating weather. They encountered broken clouds at first, then an overcast that obscured the moon. For most of the flight, they followed the tracks of the Union Pacific Railroad. Also, public-spirited citizens had lit bonfires and flares in cities along the route. Knight reported that the airfield at Omaha was so well lit that landing was as easy as in daylight.

Although the mail had reached Omaha on schedule, it seemed fated to go no farther. The weather was getting worse, and the only pilot available who knew the Omaha-Chicago route refused to fly. At this point, Knight volunteered to continue westward. He studied a map of the unfamiliar route while a DH was serviced for the trip. At 1:59 A.M., after forty-nine minutes on the ground, he left for Iowa City, intermediate stop on the route to Chicago.

There were few towns between Omaha and Des Moines, so Knight steered a compass course for the first hundred miles. Visibility remained good, and he was able to identify Des Moines without difficulty, flying over the lighted dome of the capitol. "Altogether, the first half of the trip was all right," Knight later told a reporter. "But I got pretty lonesome. At times the moon was totally obscured by a heavy black layer of clouds. It looked as if the whole blooming world was sleeping hard, and Oh man, I envied most of them. . . . There's a sense of isolation that's hard to describe."

As Knight headed toward Iowa City, a layer of clouds began to drift underneath the plane, threatening to obscure the ground. "I didn't dare lose sight of the ground," Knight reported, "so I dropped down from half a mile to fly at 100 feet." The air was rough at this low altitude. Fog obscured the valley, and snow flurries restricted visibility. Knight picked up the railroad tracks heading toward Iowa City and struggled to keep them in sight. He managed to reach the city, but it took another twelve minutes to spot the red flares that marked the landing area. "More by luck than by skill," Knight remarked, he made a perfect landing.

INTRODUCTION

After phoning Chicago for the latest weather report, Knight decided to delay his departure from Iowa City so as to arrive over Chicago at first light. After an hour and forty-five minutes on the ground, he left Iowa City at 6:30 A.M. About one hour en route, just as he reached Clinton, ground fog began to form below him. Comforted by a streak of first light in the east, Knight decided to take a chance on improving weather ahead. "I climbed to 5,000 feet," he said, "and ran on, trusting to drop down beyond the Mississippi." He had good luck—or good weather sense. As the tired pilot approached Chicago, the fog began to break up. He quickly picked up suburban landmarks, located the airport, and landed without incident at 8:40 A.M.

Jack O. Webster then flew the mail to Cleveland, where Ernest M. Allison was waiting to take the final segment of the trip. Battling snow and sleet, the determined Allison reached New York, via a refueling stop at Bellefonte, at 4:50 P.M., February 23. Word of his arrival was flashed to Washington, where there were reports of "great jubilation" in the Post Office.

There was good reason for celebration. The Post Office had shattered the transcontinental record for mail delivery, crossing the country in thirty-three hours and twenty minutes. The previous coast-to-coast record had been seventy-two hours by special train, a time that the Air Mail Service earlier had matched by a combination of airplane and train. Especially impressive had been the nighttime operations. As Praeger pointed out, night flying would mean "the speedy revolutionizing of letter transportation methods and practices throughout the world." And this was just the beginning. Looking to the future, the *New York Herald* predicted that the day soon would come when mail would be carried across the continent in twelve hours.

While congratulations poured into the Post Office, an unimpressed House of Representatives considered airmail appropriations. Dismissing the transcontinental flight as nothing

INTRODUCTION

but "propaganda," Rep. Jasper Napoleon Tincher of Kansas argued that the House should put an end to a scandalously uneconomical enterprise and eliminate the Air Mail Service. Supporters of the airmail countered with a motion to restore full funding for the service. It went down to defeat, 221 to 121. After further debate, the House finally agreed to continue funding the Air Mail Service but only at the level of $1,250,000, as originally approved by the Appropriations Committee. The Senate accepted the House version of the bill.

When the new Republican administration took office in March, Postmaster General Will H. Hays tried to persuade the Army to take over the airmail. Fearful of inadequate funding, the military declined. The Post Office then sought to interest private enterprise in relieving the government of an unwanted responsibility. The absence of government regulation or subsidy, however, meant that profits would be doubtful, causing businesses to shy away from the offer. In the end, reluctant postal officials decided to continue operations on a limited scale until private enterprise was ready to step in.

The government went on to fly the transcontinental route between 1921 and 1927, with great success. In 1923, the Air Mail Service received the Collier Trophy, awarded annually for the greatest achievement in aviation, for flying from coast to coast for a year without a fatal accident. It won the prestigious trophy again in 1924, this time for pioneering night flying.

The success of the Air Mail Service, together with passage of the Air Commerce Act of 1926 and prospects for federal subsidy, finally lured private companies into commercial aviation. On July 1, 1927, the Post Office relinquished the San Francisco–Chicago portion of the transcontinental route to Boeing Air Transport. Two months later, National Air Transport took over the Chicago–New York portion. In the early 1930s, the two companies merged to form United Air Lines.

United continues to fly the transcontinental route between

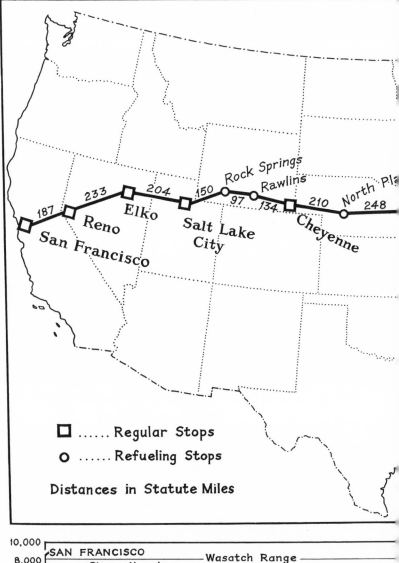

□ ..... Regular Stops

○ ..... Refueling Stops

Distances in Statute Miles

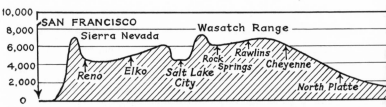

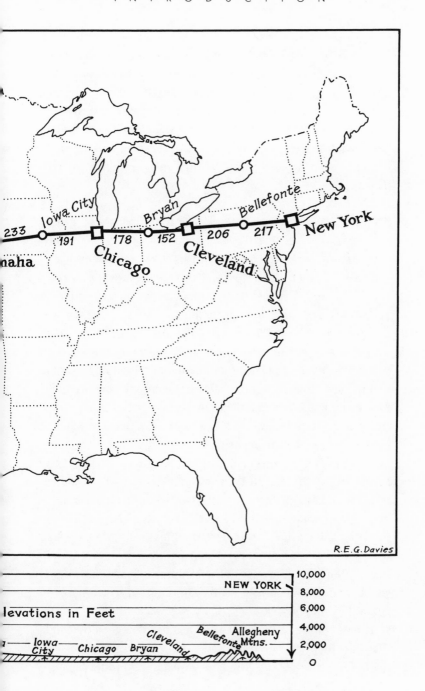

R.E.G.Davies

INTRODUCTION

New York and San Francisco. In 1990, however, DC-10s and Boeing 767s span the continent in five-and-a-half to six hours, nonstop, with 250 passengers. Sitting seven miles above the ground in a pressurized cabin, few people know—or care—about the heroic pioneers who blazed the air trail across the country. Nonetheless, as the *New York Times* observed in 1921, aviation owes a great deal to Otto Praeger and his brave young pilots who flew through wind and weather to deliver the mail.

The documents that follow speak to the nature of airmail operations during the establishment of the transcontinental route. As can be seen in "General Directions to Entire Personnel," Burleson and Praeger clearly ran a tight ship. Determined to make the airmail a regular part of postal operations and not "an experimental plaything," they demanded the "utmost conscientious effort" from all personnel.

Insisting that the mail go through despite the weather, Praeger tended to push pilots beyond the limits of existing technology. Engines often malfunctioned, causing frequent forced landings. Aeronautical compasses were so unreliable that pilots often flew without one. Airspeed indicators, using pitot-venturi tubes to measure air pressure, rarely worked, especially when ice was encountered. Altimeters featured one revolution of the dial to twenty thousand feet. Turn indicators, which first appeared in 1920, were too sensitive for flying in rough air and employed venturi tubes that clogged in icing conditions. Bank indicators used bubbles that were too small to be seen easily and that produced erratic indications even in light turbulence. "Because of their imperfections," one airman summarized, "there was a hearty contempt of instruments in general by all pilots."

At one point, the fliers rebelled against Praeger's demands that they fly whenever Washington dictated. In July 1919, two pilots refused to fly the New York–Washington route because of fog and low clouds. When Praeger ordered them fired, a number of sympathetic pilots called in "sick" and brought operations to a halt. Praeger took a hard line with the recalcitrants. The Post Office, he said, "cannot leave the question of when to fly and when not to fly in each instance to the judgment of a dozen different aviators. If this were done, it would be impossible to operate the mail schedule with any degree of dependability and the Air Mail would have to be abandoned."

The pilots, in turn, complained that Praeger, who lacked a technical background in aviation, failed to understand the problems of flying in bad weather. Nor did he seem to realize that the pilots cared as much about the success of the airmail as did postal officials.

In the end, the dispute was settled by compromise. Praeger rehired one of the fired pilots. Also, he agreed to delegate more authority to field managers. Nevertheless, as stipulated in the "General Directions," pilots still had to take an oath of office that required them to fly whenever so ordered by postal supervisors or be dismissed.

And fly they did, even without prodding from Praeger. Wesley L. Smith, one of the most determined of the postal pilots, has described the hazards the airmail pilots often faced. On April 27, 1920, he left Washington when the ceiling was only four hundred feet. Flying under low clouds, Smith encountered rain, fog, and low visibility just south of Baltimore. Running into what he described as "a bad place," he circled for fifteen minutes at treetop level before finding an opening in the fog. "All the rest of way," he reported, "I had to fly very low, sometimes as low as fifty feet, to stay below the fog and clouds." On the outskirts of Newark, he ran into dense smoke that cut forward visibility to zero. Climbing to six hundred feet, he was able to catch occasional glimpses of the ground but saw no recognizable landmarks. "Then the fog suddenly blew in around me so that I could see nothing ahead or below

INTRODUCTION

me either," Smith noted. "I just missed a huge steeple and then hit trees before I saw them." His plane plowed through the trees, hit the ground, and burst into flames. The lucky pilot escaped with only scratches and bruises, but others were not so fortunate. Between July 1919 and March 1920, four airmail pilots died in weather-related crashes.

The "General Directions" reflects the wartime roots of the Air Mail Service. Most of the pilots were trained by the military and were used to strict discipline. Although Praeger's successors, emphasizing safety, would grant pilots more authority to make operational decisions, the Air Mail Service would never be conducted in a casual fashion. The airmail, after all, was part of the Post Office, an agency that claimed "a glorious tradition" in the speedy delivery of the mail.

While planning for the transcontinental airmail, Praeger asked pilots to submit descriptions of the route. The winning entries, worth fifty dollars each, appeared in February 1921 as *Pilots' Directions: New York–San Francisco Route.* Used as a guide by the postal airmen, this historic document stands as the single most important source of information on the state of air navigation during an era when only contact flying was possible.

As pointed out by Wesley Smith, who sent in the winning entry for the New York–Cleveland route, you look for your first directional aid shortly after Hazelhurst Field: the tracks of the Long Island Railroad. Railroads later will become your primary cross-country navigational aid, but lines are so numerous east of the Mississippi River that you have to rely mainly on geographical features to find your way to Chicago.

Flying at four or five thousand feet, you pass over a series of lakes as you head westward. Crossing into Pennsylvania, you check your position by identifying towns along the route. You know that you are over New Berlin, for example, by spying the covered bridge over Penns Creek. By now, you are crossing a series of mountain ranges. The rolling country makes an emergency landing hazardous, so you listen intently for the rhythmic beat of your four-hundred-horsepower Liberty engine. (The pilot is over terrain that the press later will label the "Hell Stretch" for the number of pilots who died while carrying the mail over the Alleghenies in bad weather.)

About two hours and 185 miles from New York, you fly through Woodward Pass, directly on course for Bellefonte, your first stop. Crossing the next mountain range at Millheim, you can see the Bald Eagle Mountain Range directly ahead. Look for a gap in the range that can be identified by a clearing with a few trees scattered in it. Fly through this clearing. Bellefonte is just ahead. The airfield—a rolling field six hundred yards long by two hundred yards wide—can be found east of town, marked by a white circle.

The compass course from Bellefonte to Cleveland is 310 degrees. In order to check the accuracy of the often unreliable compass, circle over Bellefonte, then fly to a bare spot on the mountaintop south of the gap in the Bald Eagle Range. The direct line between the field and the bare spot is 310 degrees. You not only can check the compass but you also can get an idea about the wind. However, do not rely on your compass. Be sure to check your location by identifying the towns along the route.

The rolling terrain continues for the first hundred miles out of Bellefonte; then the land becomes level. As you fly over the Allegheny River at Franklin (look for the pronounced horseshoe bend in the river due south of Franklin), the country below takes on a more settled appearance, with numerous farms dotting the landscape.

The airmail field at Cleveland can be found on the eastern edge of the city, located between two railroads that follow the lakeshore. The field is in the middle of factories and is easy to miss, so look for the long cinder runway. Be careful when landing: there are high-tension wires on all sides of the field except to the east.

Leaving Cleveland, head south-southwest for about ten miles, then turn due west. This will keep you away from the city and over good emergency landing fields. Follow the shore of Lake Erie, noting the section lines that now run north-south and east-west. Cross the south end of Sandusky Bay, then follow the section lines due west. The country is open and level. If you run into a strong westerly wind and need fuel, stop at Bryan, located on the south side of the four-track New York Central Railroad.

Now locate Hamilton, which is just north of Bryan on the southern end of an irregularly shaped lake. The Wabash Railroad runs just to the south of Hamilton. Follow the tracks for the next 125 miles and you will see Lake Michigan. At Crisman (a railroad coaling station with a large black coal chute on the north side of the tracks), follow the shore of the lake, but be sure to stay about ten miles from the water's edge just in case you have to make a forced landing.

About fifteen miles from Crisman you will see Lake Calumet, the largest and most westerly of three lakes. From the north end of the lake, head northwest. Look for a large drainage canal. On your left, where the Des Plaines River enters the canal, the canal makes a 45-degree turn to the south. Follow the river for ten miles until you see a large hospital and an old racetrack. The airmail field can be identified by the two large cinder runways that form an X. The best approach is from the south because of the high-tension and telephone wires to the west and east.

Once you head west from Chicago, the railroad becomes your primary navigational aid for crossing the plains. Just after takeoff, pick up the third railroad north of the field. By keeping on the section lines, you can follow the double-tracked Chicago & North Western for 191 miles to Iowa City. Railroads also mark the course from Iowa City to Omaha via Des Moines.

The route from Omaha to Cheyenne, pilot James Murray observed, "is one of the most pleasant over which to fly." The land rises gradually from one thousand feet at Omaha to six thousand feet at Cheyenne, and there are good emergency

INTRODUCTION

landing fields all along the way. "One can fly this route when fog and clouds are only 200 feet above the ground," Murray notes. However, the weather generally is good, especially between North Platte and Cheyenne.

Navigation is easy. Climbing to five thousand feet after leaving Omaha, you can keep the Platte River in view to a refueling stop at North Platte, 248 miles away. Also, you can follow the double tracks of the Union Pacific Railroad directly to the airfield at North Platte. Because North Platte is almost due west of Omaha, you also can fly along an east-west section line, checking your compass and getting a wind correction.

Leaving North Platte, follow the south branch of the Platte River for fifty miles to Ogallala—a famous stop on the old cattle trail from Texas. Now head due west to Chappell, forty miles away, where you once again pick up the Union Pacific and follow it to Cheyenne. The airfield is due north of the capitol building, an unmistakable landmark with a gilded dome. Watch your landing. As the *Pilots' Directions* warns, the thin air makes rough landings the rule rather than the exception.

The route between Cheyenne and Salt Lake City, especially west of the Laramie Valley, is one of the most challenging segments of the transcontinental airway. Harry G. Smith, who submitted the winning description of the route, advises pilots to use a map that accurately shows the location of mountain ranges and peaks (he favors the Rand McNally Pocket Map). "If you are not perfectly familiar with the route," he counsels, "it is almost impossible to fly without a good map." Do not trust your compass: "I find that due to the side winds and the inaccuracy of most of the compasses it is impossible to fly by compass alone."

Smith goes on to describe the conditions often found between Cheyenne and Salt Lake City:

The greatest difficulties encountered along this route are the wind, the storms, and clouds. The wind is especially bad between Cheyenne and Rock Springs. It quite often attains the velocity of 50 miles per hour on the ground. To make any head way against this it is necessary to fly very close to the ground. It is almost always from the west. The clouds and storms are quite often bad in the mountains just east of Salt Lake. We often have to try several different passes before finding one that is free from clouds.

You must fly over a series of mountain ranges after leaving Cheyenne. Taking the less direct course, climb to nine thousand feet in order to cross the Laramie Mountains, some twelve miles west of the airfield. You then enter a wide valley with good emergency fields. Follow the Union Pacific tracks to Laramie, passing six miles to the north of the town. Ahead, Elk Mountain, at the northern end of the Medicine Bow Range, stands out. Cross to the north of this twelve-thousand-foot mountain, and again follow the Union Pacific over rough country to the emergency field at Rawlins.

The course between Rawlins and the refueling stop at Rock Springs parallels the tracks of the Union Pacific. The country is rough, broken with washouts and gulches. Heavy sagebrush covers the level stretches. The airmail field at Rock Springs is at the foot of Pilot Butte, a whitish stone formation about four miles north of town.

The route from Rock Springs to Salt Lake City is easy to follow, as the unmistakable double tracks of the Union Pacific will take you to Coalville, twenty-five miles from Salt Lake City. The problem on this segment of the route is the terrain. There are few good emergency landing fields between Rock Springs and Coalville. After Coalville, the route crosses the forbidding Wasatch Range. Smith recommends a minimum altitude of eleven thousand feet for the final twenty-five miles of the route.

"Almost before he realizes it," Smith notes, the pilot "is over

Salt Lake Valley and the city itself. With a sigh of relief he begins to peer through the habitual smoke and haze of the city for the field." Locate the airstrip two miles west of town, near the fairgrounds. Be sure to land north or south, and look out for the high-tension wires that border the field on every side except to the north.

Departing Salt Lake City, fly due west across the southern end of the Great Salt Lake. The railroad again points the way to Reno. Approximately two hours from Salt Lake City, cross the East Humboldt Range at Secret Pass. There is a refueling field at Elko, thirty miles ahead in the Humboldt Valley. Less than an hour's flying time west of Elko, you encounter uninhabited desert country. Rather than fly the direct course, it is wiser to follow the Southern Pacific Railroad. If you are forced down, only the railroad can provide emergency assistance. Finally, 233 lonely miles from Elko, Reno appears under your wing.

When you leave Reno, try to take off to the east. There is a slight downgrade in that direction, helping you reach flying speed more quickly in the thin air of 4,497 feet. After takeoff, head southwest and climb to ten thousand feet over the field. You will need the altitude to cross the majestic Sierra Nevadas. As one pilot remarked, "A missing motor here will make a flyer's hair crawl around in his helmet." Follow the Southern Pacific over the mountains to the Sacramento Valley. The railroad will take you almost to Oakland. Pass over the city, then fly directly across San Francisco Bay to the old fairgrounds on the south side of the bay, three miles from the Golden Gate. Land east-west, and look out for the ever-present high-tension wires.

N eedless to say, the transcontinental route could be demanding in good weather. In bad weather, pilots had to call upon all their hard-earned skills to carry the mail to its destination. Between January 1922 and June

I N T R O D U C T I O N

1927, postal airmen flew over fourteen million miles along the transcontinental route, carrying more than 250,000,000 letters. They set an unequaled standard of excellence for long-distance operations, as they laid the foundations for the rapid growth of the American air transport industry that took place during the 1930s.

GENERAL DIRECTIONS TO ENTIRE PERSONNEL

[D E C E M B E R   1 9 2 0]

I t is the earnest desire of the Post Office Department that every employee of the Air Mail Service become a living example of the spirit which dominates mail transportation and which years of service has developed into a glorious tradition. This spirit is well expressed in the following quotation which covers the entire cornice of the New York City Post Office:

> Neither snow nor rain nor heat
> nor gloom of night stays these couriers
> from the swift completion of their
> appointed rounds.

Our branch of the service is the newest and swiftest. It will no doubt become the most important branch for the rapid transportation of valuable mail. It is our duty to see that it takes equal rank with other methods of mail transportation in respect to safety and reliability. To accomplish this, we must keep constantly in mind: (a) that carrying the mail by airplane is a government enterprise of greatest importance, (b) that it is a great commercial operation for obtaining maximum results with a minimum cost, and is not in any sense an experimental plaything, and (c) that to make a record which will compare favorably with that of the other branches of our service, the utmost conscientious effort must be exerted by every individual employee and the whole effort must be one of hearty co-operation which is an absolute essential of success. In order that a proper co-ordination of our work may be accomplished, the Department invites the study of the following rules and directions. They are to be strictly observed as far as humanly possible. Suggestions or criticisms will be welcome.

GENERAL ORGANIZATION

Chief Executive: The organization of the Post Office Department, under the law, makes the Second Assistant Postmaster General the executive head of air mail transportation. He is therefore, under the Postmaster General, the chief executive of the Air Mail Service. The law requires his approval on all matters involving the expenditure of money, the making of appointments, dismissals and promotions, and the policies of the service. He maintains general supervision of all matters.

Superintendent of Operations: A superintendent of operations, appointed by the Second Assistant Postmaster General, is the active director of the Air Mail Service. The headquarters staff and all field officers are under his immediate direction.

Division Superintendents: The present organization provides a division superintendent for specified sections of the route. The division superintendents are directly responsible to the Superintendent of Operations.

Field Managers: In direct charge of the personnel and activities of each field, and responsible to their respective division superintendents, are the field managers. All personnel, including pilots while stationed at or on their fields, are subject to the orders of the field manager.

Pilots: The selection and employment of all pilots is made by a Chief of Flying, who will also make the necessary assignments to duty and station to meet the needs of the various division superintendents. While pilots are always subject to the prior and higher orders of division superintendents, they are also under the direction of the field managers of the particular station which is their headquarters or on which they may be in the performance of their duty.

RULES AND REGULATIONS
GOVERNING PILOTS

1. OATHS OF OFFICE

(a) The following is a copy of your oath of office. "I do further solemnly swear that I will faithfully perform all the duties required of me, and abstain from everything forbidden by the laws in relation to the establishment of post offices and post roads within the United States; and that I will honestly and truly account for and pay over any money belonging to the said United States which may come into my possession or control. So help me God."

(b) The following is your agreement on appointment: "I hereby make application for position of pilot in the Air Mail Service and hereby agree, if appointed, to fly whenever called upon and in whatever Air Mail plane that I may be directed by the superintendent of the division to which I am assigned, or his representative on the field, and in the event of my refusal to fly, such refusal shall constitute my resignation from the service, which you are hereby authorized to accept. If appointed, I pledge myself to serve the Air Mail Service of the Post Office Department for a period of one year, and to carry out its orders implicitly, unless separated for cause or in accordance with the foregoing agreement, provided that if I desire to leave the service I will not do so without having first given the Department fifteen days' notice of my intended separation."

(c) These quotations are given so that all pilots may familiarize themselves with the oath taken and their fundamental duties to the United States Government through the Post Office Department. Pilots will interpret all orders in the light of these pledges which they have taken to sustain government institutions.

(d) All pilots who have not already done so will furnish this Bureau with a $1000 bond. This bond is required of all postal employees handling mail.

2. STATUS OF PILOTS

(a) *Probationary Pilot*: A pilot will be considered on probation during the period from date of appointment to date of assignment to a division, unless he is designated for a special duty. Such pilots are under the direct supervision of the Chief of Flying and will take up all official matters directly through him. A special order covering this status reads: "All pilots while waiting for assignment to active flying duty in the Air Mail Service following appointment will place themselves at the disposal of the field manager under whom they are stationed. The field manager has the authority to assign such men to various field duties at all times that dual or solo flights are not being made by each individual pilot."

3. GENERAL AIMS

(a) The *most important duty* of all pilots, first, last, and always, is to get the *mail* entrusted to him to its *destination* on *schedule* time.

GENERAL   DIRECTIONS

4. CONDUCT

(a) All pilots should so conduct themselves as to be in the finest condition both mentally and physically, both for self-protection and for the protection of the valuable property assigned to them.

(b) As a pilot in the Air Mail Service, you represent the Post Office Department, and as such a representative you will be courteous, and will act the part of a gentleman at all times.

(c) A part of the pilot's rating will be based on the promptness with which he reports for the various duties assigned him.

(d) Pilots will obey all orders from the Second Assistant Postmaster General, Superintendent of Operations or Chief of Flying through the division superintendent to whom they are assigned, promptly, or suitable disciplinary action will follow.

5. GENERAL RULES FOR PILOTS

(1) Pilots shall not perform stunts with mail airplanes, nor put them to unnecessary strains in service.

(2) Pilots shall not carry passengers in mail airplanes except by authority of the Second Assistant Postmaster General or the Superintendent of Operations.

(3) Under no circumstances will the weight of mail be reduced to take on a passenger unless by specific order of the superintendent.

(4) When proper authority has been granted for passengers to be carried on a mail trip, the representative at the starting point should place his o.k. on the letter authorizing flight, and when the destination is reached by the aviator and passenger, the passenger will then affix his signature on the letter of au-

G E N E R A L   D I R E C T I O N S

thorization and the representative will then forward it to the Division of Air Mail Service for the files.

(5) Pilots are expected to report at the flying field early enough to make reasonable inspections of the ships they are to fly, and to assure themselves that the motors are being properly warmed up.

(6) Pilots shall see that emergency tool kits are placed in the airplanes and will be responsible for their absence, unless they have made complaint to the manager before departure. (Get plane inspection card from manager.)

(7) Pilots shall fly at safe altitudes, weather permitting. As the safe altitude varies with the character of the country and the type of the airplane flown, no altitude can be here specified.

(8) Maps shall be carried, unless the pilots are absolutely certain of the routes.

(9) Pilots must observe compasses, even when not flying by compass, as the compass very easily gets out of adjustment, and cannot be kept accurate without constant observation and recompensation. Pilots are therefore directed to check up course and compass on each flight and report compass readings and approximate deviation.

(10) Pilots landing with mail have the right of way.

(11) In making out pilots' reports, pilots will carefully set down all the information requested and such other information, regarding the condition of the airplane, motor, or weather, as they deem important or helpful.

(12) The Air Mail Service is run on schedule. Pilots will therefore report, on the "Pilots Report" card, the cause of any delay in starting in excess of ten minutes.

(13) Pilots shall make every effort to arrive on schedule time. This means that the motor must be pushed against a headwind.

G E N E R A L   D I R E C T I O N S

(14) Pilots will locate likely fields at every opportunity, reporting location and description to the division headquarters.

(15) Each pilot will familiarize himself at once with all characteristics of all flying fields which he must use in line of duty. No excuse will be accepted for "crashing" a ship on a home field when it is evident that pilot "crashed" through lack of knowledge of local conditions.

(16) On account of the fact that the varying conditions at the various fields prevent drawing up a standard set of field rules, pilots shall familiarize themselves with the local field rules obtaining at each station and be guided accordingly.

6.   PREPARATION FOR FLIGHT

(1) The pilot should inspect his ship *thoroughly*, reporting any defects to the chief mechanic in sufficient time to permit of correction before flight is scheduled.

(2) Pilots must be present or in the cockpit when motor is "warmed up."

(3) The following rules will be followed in starting the Liberty 12 motor:

1st Close radiator shutters.

2nd Retard spark and close throttle.

3rd Turn on gasoline.

4th Pump up three pounds pressure.

5th Prime motor; i.e., turn on gasoline petcock to priming pump, pull plunger out *slowly* and discharge quickly; *THREE* times for *COLD* motor and *ONCE ONLY* for *WARM* motor.

6th CLOSE gasoline petcock to priming pump.

7th Turn motor over four times.

8th Crank motor with ONE switch ONLY (SEE NOTE).

9th After starting, open throttle slightly and advance spark about half way.

G E N E R A L   D I R E C T I O N S

10th Run motor at 450 to 500 RPM until water is at 40 to
45 degrees centigrade and oil pressure about 10 lbs.
Then run at 1000 RPM until water is at 60 to 65
degrees and oil pressure about 20 lbs. (SEE NOTE).

11th Test ignition through each switch. Determine setting
of spark for maximum RPM.

12th Open the shutters.

13th Use spark setting determined above for climbing.

14th Never run motor 1400 RPM on ground longer than
necessary to read tachometer for determination of
spark setting.

> *NOTE*: Generator reaches voltage at about 750
> RPM. *NEVER* use two switches below 750.
> *ALWAYS* use two switches about 750.

7. FORCED LANDINGS

(a) Immediately upon making a forced landing the pilot will
put in telephone calls to the two fields nearest him, giving the
following information to the field first answering:

1. Place of landing;
2. Time of landing;
3. Reason for landing;
4. Possibility of continuing flight;
5. Possibility of landing another plane nearby and taking
off again with the mail;
6. Approximate time mail can be sent by train;
7. Amount of damage, if any, and possibility of flying the
plane out with minor repairs.

(b) The pilot making a forced landing must also stay with the
plane and attend to the following:

1. *Disposal of mail*—reshipment by air or rail in
accordance with orders transmitted from the
superintendent;

2. *Provisions for guarding the plane against further damage*:
   a. Providing a watchman;
   b. Moving plane to take advantage of shelter if possible, and tying down to avoid damage from wind;
   c. Draining of water and oil in cold water [weather];
   d. Removal of clock, compass, log book and tools to places of safety in case of wreck.

(c) If the ship cannot be readily repaired, or is inaccessible, before turning over to watchman—

1. In cold weather, drain all water by removing plug at bottom of radiator and in pump casting. Turn prop to be sure pump is thoroughly drained. Then *replace* plugs;
2. Stake down ship in best manner possible to prevent damage by wind;
3. Lash controls in neutral position to prevent wind damage;
4. Disconnect main lead at battery terminal. (Curious visitors cannot then manipulate switch and drain battery, injure generator or start engine).

To cover watchman's compensation, pilots must carry on *every* flight "Contract Memorandum" blanks, and "Bill for Service Rendered or Material Purchased" blanks, furnished by managers of stations. Pay for watchman is not to exceed 35 cents per hour and for transporting mail from forced landing to railroad station, 25 cents per mile.

The pilot will then proceed to the point to which he is ordered to report, but should not leave the point of landing without *specific orders.*

(d) It is understood that there will be emergencies in which it will be impracticable to comply fully with the above instructions. In such cases, pilots must use their best judgment and keep in mind these three points:

1. The mail must be forwarded the quickest way possible, preferably by air;
2. The airplane must be guarded from loss or further damage;
3. The superintendent must be informed of all the circumstances as soon as possible.

(e) Pilots will be required to turn in *written* reports of all forced landings upon getting back to their home station. These reports shall give:

1. Place, date and time of landing;
2. Cause of landing and results;
3. Procedure following the landing;
4. Estimate of damage to the plane;
5. Estimated damage to property on which the plane landed. Also brief description of damage.

8. ASSIGNMENT TO STATION

(a) Where possible, preference on changes of station will be based on relative satisfactory time in the service.

9. REPORTS

(a) Pilots will fill out "Pilot's Daily Report" promptly on the completion of every flight, on the *same report card on which he* [sic] *signed the inspection sheet* when accepting the airplane at a station before flight.

(b) Written report must be made on every forced landing, as described in 7-e. Time of landing and departure must be stated specifically both for ship and for mail, in case it is dispatched by train, always obtaining receipt for mail if delivered to any Post Office or railroad clerk.

10. EXPENSE ACCOUNTS

Under Order No. 3434 of the Postmaster General, pilots are

GENERAL   DIRECTIONS

allowed "in addition to their regular salary, their expenses for lodging and subsistence not to exceed one dollar and fifty cents ($1.50) for each one-way trip flown over the route to which they are assigned, in connection with the operation and maintenance of aeroplanes." In the preparation of expense accounts under this order, which contemplates only flights which are completed between designated termini, an itemized statement of expenses will not be required, nor will vouchers be necessary to cover lodging at outer termini of their runs. All mail trips or trips by plane should be so indicated on the accounts.

If, however, a pilot starts on his mail trip, but fails to complete same because of forced landing or other accident, he is not entitled to the $1.50 expense allowance for the trip, but is entitled to actual expenses not to exceed $3.00 per day for subsistence, and in addition reimbursement for such railroad fare, less war tax, and emergency expenditures as may be necessary, in which case vouchers must be submitted to cover items for lodging, railroad fare and emergency purchases. In cases of this kind, and in all other cases involving travel away from headquarters on official business, on other than assigned trips by plane, pilots will be governed by instructions to employees generally relative to the preparation and submission of expense accounts.

The $1.50 allowance per trip flown over the route is not a bonus, but an allowance for subsistence, and is all that is allowed for subsistence expenses chargeable to that day, of which lodging is a part, and while it may be insufficient to entirely cover expenses incident to the outbound trip, it is believed that the allowance for the route trip will average sufficient to cover all necessary expenses.

PILOTS'
DIRECTIONS
NEW YORK–
SAN FRANCISCO
ROUTE

DISTANCES, LANDMARKS, COMPASS COURSE,
EMERGENCY AND REGULAR LANDING FIELDS,
WITH SERVICE AND COMMUNICATION
FACILITIES AT PRINCIPAL POINTS ON ROUTE

POST OFFICE DEPARTMENT,
OFFICE OF SECOND ASSISTANT POSTMASTER GENERAL,
DIVISION OF AIR MAILS.

These flying directions and the ground information were prepared with the cooperation of pilots and supervisory officials of the Air Mail Service and with the assistance of the postmasters located within 5 miles of the line of flight. All employees of the Air Mail Service will be required to familiarize themselves with the information relating to the section of the route with which they are concerned.

Otto Praeger,
Second Assistant Postmaster General.

Washington, D.C.,
February 20, 1921.

TRANSCONTINENTAL

AIR MAIL

PILOTS' LOG OF DISTANCES,

LANDMARKS, AND FLYING

DIRECTIONS

I

NEW YORK TO BELLEFONTE

Miles.

0. *Hazelhurst Field, Long Island.*—Follow the tracks of the Long Island Railroad past Belmont Park race track, keeping Jamaica on the left. Cross New York over the lower end of Central Park.

25. *Newark, N.J.*—Heller Field is located in Newark and may be identified as follows: The field is 1¼ miles west of the Passaic River and lies in the V formed by the Greenwood Lake Division and Orange branch of the New York, Lake Erie & Western Railroad. The Morris Canal bounds the western edge of the field. The roof of the large steel hangar is painted an orange color.

30. *Orange Mountains.*—Cross the Orange Mountains over a small round lake or pond. Slightly to the right will be seen the polo field and golf course of Essex Country Club. About 8 miles to the north is Mountain Lake, easily seen after crossing the Orange Mountains.

50. *Morristown, N.J.*—About 4 miles north of course. Identified by a group of yellow buildings east of the city. The Delaware, Lackawanna & Western Railroad passes the eastern side of Morristown.

60. *Lake Hopatcong.*—A large irregular lake 10 miles north of course.

64. *Budd Lake.*—Large circular body of water 6 miles north of course.

78. *Belvidere, N.J.*—On the Delaware River. Twelve miles to the north is the Delaware Water Gap and 11 miles to the south is Easton at the junction of the Lehigh and Delaware Rivers. The Delaware makes a pronounced U-shaped bend just north of Belvidere. A railway joins the two ends of the U.

111. *Lehighton, Pa.*—Directly on the course. The Lehigh Valley and Central Railroad of New Jersey, running parallel, pass through Lehighton. The Lehigh River runs between the railroads at this point. Lehighton is approximately halfway between Hazelhurst and Bellefonte. A fair size elliptical race track lies just southwest of town but a larger and better emergency landing field lies about 100 yards west of the race track. The field is very long and lies in a north-south direction.

114. *Mauch Chunk.*—Three miles north of Lehighton and on the direct course.

121. *Central Railroad of New Jersey.*—Two long triangular bodies of water northwest of the railroad followed by eight or nine small artificial lakes or ponds about half a mile apart almost parallel with the course but veering slightly to the south.

148. *Catawissa Mountain Range,* which appears to curve in a semi-circle about a large open space of country directly on the course. To the north of the course may be seen the eastern branch of the Susquehanna. Fly parallel to this until Shamokin Creek is picked up. This creek is very black and is paralleled by two railroads. Shamokin Creek empties into the Susquehanna just below Sunbury.

168. *Sunbury, Pa.*—At the junction of the two branches of the Susquehanna River. The infield of a race track on a small island at the junction of the two rivers furnishes a good landing field. The river to the south of Sunbury is wider than to the north and is filled with numerous small islands. The two branches to the north have practically no islands. If the river is reached and Sunbury is not in sight look for islands. If there are none, follow the river

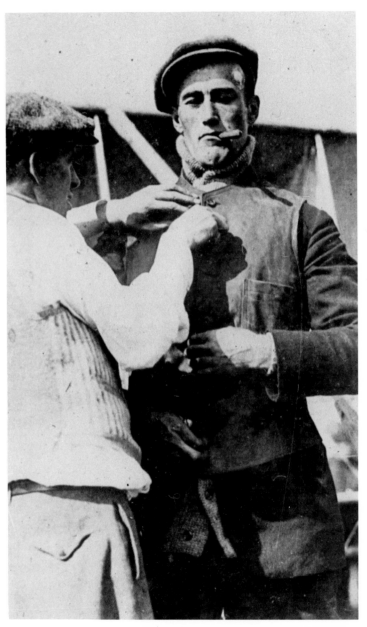

Cigar clamped firmly in mouth, Cal Rodgers gets ready for another day's flying.

*This promotional poster appeared throughout the country
following the successful flight of the* Vin Fiz.

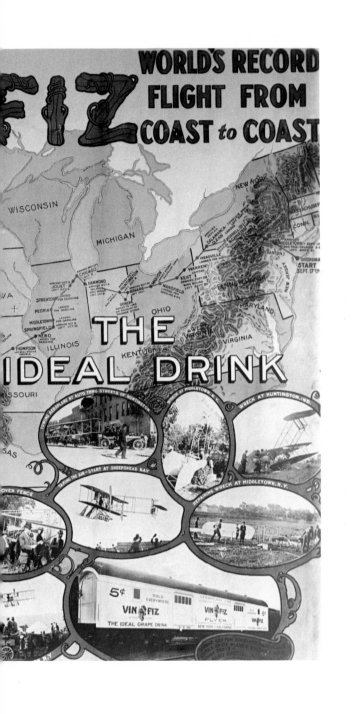

The Vin Fiz *suffers one of many accidents on its way across the continent: Huntington, Indiana, October 2; 1911.*

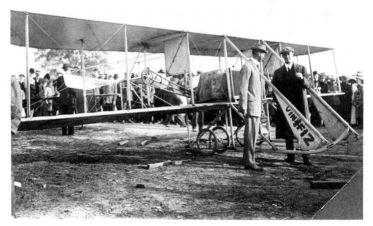

Cal Rodgers, on right, at Pasadena, California, at the end of his transcontinental adventure.

Brig. Gen. William "Billy" Mitchell.

Lt. Belvin W. Maynard, winner of the transcontinental air race, climbs into the cockpit of his DH-4. Sgt. William E. Kline holds Maynard's dog, Trixie. Both Kline and Trixie made the round-trip crossing of the continent.

From left: Washington postmaster Merritt O. Chance, Postmaster General Albert S. Burleson, and President Woodrow Wilson at the inauguration of the Washington–New York airmail route, Polo Field, Washington, D.C., May 15, 1918.

Lt. George L. Boyle in a Curtiss Jenny prepares to get under way from Polo Field on May 15, 1918. He never reached Philadelphia.

Otto Praeger.

First flight on the reopened New York–Cleveland portion of the transcontinental route, May 15, 1919. Pilot Frank Stark arrives in Cleveland, where mechanic Henry Wacker unloads the mail.

An accident at Chicago, June 16, 1919. Pilot Trent Fry escaped without injury.

Randolph G. Page strapped a suitcase full of letters to the lower wing of his DH-4 at the inauguration of transcontinental service on September 8, 1920.

The transcontinental mail arrives at Rock Springs, Wyoming, September 10, 1920. James P. Murray is the pilot.

Transferring the mail at Reno, Nevada.

The disappointing twin-DH under tow.

Mechanics at Omaha work on the engine of one of the Post Office's ill-fated JL-6s.

Omaha, 1921: a DH-4 acclaimed for having made only four forced landings (two for bad weather and two for engine trouble) in five hundred flying hours.

Post Office DH-4s at Omaha.

Loading the transcontinental mail at Omaha.

A rare picture of a DH-4 in flight.

*James P. Murray flew the western portion of the
transcontinental route for many years.*

*Jack Knight, hero of the first day-and-night transcontinental
airmail.*

*Jack O. Webster flew the Chicago–Cleveland leg of the
record-breaking transcontinental flight of February 22–23, 1921.*

*Ernest M. Allison, the unsung hero of the transcontinental flight
of February 22–23, 1921. He flew the final leg of the route, from
Cleveland to New York, in bad weather.*

*Howard C. Brown, one of thirty-four pilots who died while on
duty with the U.S. Air Mail Service, was killed on December 6,
1923, while carrying the mail between Cleveland and Chicago.*

*The popular James F. "Dinty" Moore crashed and was killed on
December 24, 1923, en route from North Platte to Cheyenne.*

Veteran airmail pilot Wesley L. Smith submitted the winning description of the New York–Cleveland route for Pilots' Directions.

In 1927 National Air Transport took over the eastern half of the transcontinental route from the U.S. Air Mail Service. It later became part of United Air Lines. The busy scene is at Chicago in 1928.

*William C. Hopson and many other experienced Post Office
pilots went with National Air Transport in 1927. Hopson was
killed on October 18, 1928, while carrying the night mail from
New York to Chicago.*

United Air Lines DC-10s now fly the transcontinental route in less than six hours.

south to Sunbury. If islands are numerous, follow the river north to Sunbury.

170. *Lewisburg, Pa.*—Two miles west of Sunbury and 8 miles north.

174. After leaving Sunbury the next landmark to pick up is Penns Creek, which empties into the Susquehanna 7 miles south of Sunbury. Flying directly on the course, Penns Creek is reached 6 miles after it joins the Susquehanna 7 miles south of Sunbury.

178. *New Berlin.*—Identified by covered bridge over Penns Creek.

185. *The Pennsylvania Railroad* from Lewisburg is crossed at the point where the range of mountains coming up from the southwest ends. The highway leaves the railroad here and goes up into Woodward Pass, directly on the course. A white fire tower may be seen on the crest of the last mountain to the north on leaving the pass.

202. The next range of mountains is crossed through the pass at Millheim, a small town. A lone mountain may be seen to the south just across the Pennsylvania tracks.

217. *Bellefonte, Pa.*—After crossing another mountain range without a pass Bellefonte will be seen against the Bald Eagle Mountain Range. On top of a mountain, just south of a gap in the Bald Eagle Range at Bellefonte, may be seen a clearing with a few trees scattered in it. This identifies this gap from others in the same range. The mail field lies just east of town and is marked by a large white circle. A white line marks the eastern edge of the field where there is a drop of nearly 100 feet.

Miles.

0. *Bellefonte.*—Compass course to Cleveland approximately 310°. Fly directly toward and over bare spot on mountain top south of gap in Bald Eagle Range. First range of mountains.

3. *Pennsylvania Railroad,* following course of Bald Eagle Creek.

17. *New York Central Railroad,* following course of Moshannon Creek.

35. *Clearfield, Pa.*—On west branch of Susquehanna River. A small race track here serves as an emergency landing field. Two railroads, one from the north and one from the east, enter Clearfield and both go south from here.

55. *C. & M. Junction.*—One branch of the Buffalo, Rochelle & Pittsburgh from the east forms a junction here with the N. & S. line of the Buffalo, Rochelle & Pittsburgh Railroad. Dubois is 2 miles north of course on the N. & S. line of this railroad.

70. *Brookville.*—One mile north of course, west of city, is 2-mile race track which makes an excellent emergency field.

86. *Clarion.*—One mile north of course. Emergency field marked by white cross and red-brick hangar is here. The Clarion River passes north edge of city. Railroad from the east ends here.

110. *Franklin, Pa.*—Seven miles north of course at junction of Allegheny River and French Creek. Cross Allegheny River where there is a pronounced horseshoe bend. This is due south of Franklin.

122. *Sandy Lake.*—Two miles north of course. Cross the Pennsylvania Railroad at right angles 2 miles south of Sandy Lake.

138. *Shenango.*—Two miles north of course. Three railroads enter this town from the north. Two continue south and one runs east for 3 miles and then turns southeast.

152. *New York Central Railroad,* running north and south. One mile north of course the Erie crosses the New York Central at right angles. Four miles west the Erie should be crossed where it turns southward. Eight miles south of course is Warren, with eight railroads radiating out.
157. *Pennsylvania Railroad,* running north and south.
165. *Baltimore & Ohio Railroad,* running diagonally north-east-southwest.
206. *Cleveland on Lake Erie.*—The mail field is in East Cleveland between the two railroads that follow the lake shore. The field is near the edge of the city and near the edge of the freight yards of the New York Central. The field is distinctly marked by long cinder runway. The air mail hangar is in the southwest corner of the field. The Martin factory is in the northwest corner of the field.

CLEVELAND TO BELLEFONTE

Miles.

0. *Cleveland, Ohio.*—Fly approximately 130° compass course.
49. *Warren.*—Eight miles south of course with eight railroads radiating out. Three of these railroads are crossed at 7-mile intervals, the third one turning east where the course crosses it, and crosses a fourth 5 miles farther on.
58. The junction of the Erie Railroad and New York Central is about 2 miles north of the course. The Erie from the point where it was crossed, 8 miles north of Warren and 3 miles east, runs eastward in the general direction of the course for about 15 miles.
68. *Shenango, Pa.*—Two miles north of course on Shenango River. Three railroads enter Shenango from the north, two continue south, while one runs east for 3 miles and then southeast. This railroad should be crossed diagonally at Kremis Station, 5 miles east of Shenango.
84. *Sandy Lake.*—Two miles north of course. Cross Pennsylvania Railroad at right angles 2 miles south of Sandy Lake.
96. *Franklin, Pa.*—Seven miles north of course at junction

of French Creek and Allegheny River. The Allegheny should be crossed 7 miles south of Franklin, where the river makes a pronounced horseshoe bend. There is an emergency landing field at Franklin used by a passenger-carrying outfit. Flying directly on the course the river is crossed four times.

120. *Clarion, Pa.*—One mile north of course. Emergency field east of city marked by red-brick hangar with white cross on the roof. Large field, but always soft after rains.

136. *Brookville, Pa.*—One mile north of course. West of city is 2-mile race track that serves as an excellent emergency landing field.

147. *Reynoldsville, Pa.*—One mile south of course on Pennsylvania Railroad, which follows Sandy Lick Creek from Brookville. The Pennsylvania crosses the course above Reynoldsville, running in a north-south direction.

151. *Dubois, Pa.*—Three miles north of course on Buffalo, Rochester & Pittsburgh Railroad. A branch of this railroad from the east forms the C. & M. Junction directly on the course. Follow this eastern branch of the railroad for about 5 miles, as it is directly on the course.

171. *Clearfield, Pa.*—On the west branch of the Susquehanna River. A small race track here can be used as an emergency field, although it is rather small. Two railroads, one from the north and one from the east, converge 1 mile east of Clearfield, enter Clearfield, and continue southward.

196. *Snowshoe, Pa.*—Seven miles north of course. A small race track may be seen here. Halfway between Clearfield and Bellefonte the course crosses Moshannon Creek. The New York Central crosses this creek directly on the course. Cross the Bald Eagle Range through the pass, and Bellefonte will be seen in the valley beyond.

206. *Bellefonte, Pa.*—The field is east of Bellefonte and is marked by a large white circle. A white line marks the eastern edge of the field, east of which is a deep ravine.

III

CLEVELAND TO CHICAGO

Miles.

0. *Martin Field, Cleveland.*—Fly a little west of south for nearly 10 miles or about seven minutes flying and then due west, thus keeping over good emergency landing fields. The country between Cleveland and Chicago is divided into sections, section lines running due north and south and east and west. For the first 15 miles the lake shore is only a few miles north of the course.

20. *Elyria, Ohio.*—Five miles south of course. Five railroads radiate out of Elyria.

37. *Vermilion.*—Two miles north of the course. On Lake Erie. The New York Central Railroad follows the shore line of the lake from Vermilion to Sandusky.

55. *Sandusky.*—Five miles north of the course on Sandusky Bay, a large irregular body of water crossed by the New York Central Railroad. Continues due west from this point, following the east-west section lines.

112. *Maumee River*, which you cross about 5 miles northeast of Grand Rapids and 5 miles south of Waterville. Waterville is on the east bank of the Maumee and Grand Rapids is on the south bank of the river where it turns east and parallels the course for 7 miles.

130. *Detroit, Toledo & Ironton Railroad*, crossed at right angles. Wausen is 7 miles north of the course and Napoleon is 5 miles south, both on the above-mentioned railroad. By flying about 11 miles north from the point where the Maumee River is crossed and then due west the New York Central four-track railroad will be picked up just before reaching Bryan.

152. *Bryan* is located on the south side of the New York Central tracks, where they are crossed by the Chicago & North Western and Northern Railroads. Landing field with hangar and T cinder runway is north of town. Field is two-way, 2,000 feet east and west. Best approach from the east.

172. *Hamilton.*—Two miles north of course and 4 miles north of Bryan. On the extreme south end of irregular-shaped lake. The Wabash Railroad runs to the south of Hamilton. By keeping the Wabash Railroad in sight for the next 125 miles, you will come in sight of Lake Michigan.

196. *Walcottville.*—At the intersection of the Wabash and Grand Rapids & Indiana Railroads.

220. *Goshen, Ind.*—Three miles north of course. The Chicago & St. Louis Railroad is crossed at right angles 3 miles south and 1 mile east of Goshen.

243. *South Bend, Ind.*—Seven miles north of course. The Chicago & St. Louis Railroad is crossed at right angles 7 miles south of South Bend.

265. *La Porte, Ind.*—One mile north of course. The New York Central Railroad running east from La Porte parallels the course to the lower edge of Lake Michigan.

289. *Crisman, Ind.*—Coaling station with large black coal chute north side of track; has also large race track with course 3½ miles north and 1½ miles east. Baltimore & Ohio Railroad crosses Wabash at Crisman. Leaving Crisman fly westerly, following shore of the lake, but keeping about 10 miles from waters edge to insure safe emergency landing.

314. *Lake Calumet.*—Largest and most westerly of three lakes. From northern extremity of Lake Calumet fly northwest on compass course of 315° Ashburn Field comes into view to the west and a large gas reservoir to the east. A large drainage canal will be seen ahead. To your left, where the Des Plaines River enters the drainage canal, the canal makes a 45° turn to the south. Follow the Des Plaines River for about 10 miles and you will see a large hospital and old race track. This is the speedway and adjoins the air-mail field on the west.

330. *Chicago air-mail field or Checkerboard field.*—Three large air-mail hangars in southwest corner of field and private hangar in northeast corner. Four-way field, but best approach from the south. Telephone and high-

tension wires to west and wires and trees to east of field. Land on large cinder runways. Sewage-disposal plant with excavations on west side of field. Landing area of this field large and ample. Telegraph and post-office address of this is Maywood, Ill. Field is 14 miles west of Chicago post office.

I V

CHICAGO TO OMAHA

Miles.

0. *Maywood, Ill.*—Checkerboard field. Fly directly west, picking up the third railroad to the north of the field. This is the Chicago & North Western. By keeping on the section lines and flying directly west this railroad can be kept in sight at all times until Iowa City is reached. It has white ballast and is doubled-tracked.

14. *Wheaton.*—Directly on course. Town rests in elongated U formed by Chicago & North Western Railroad. Water tower serves as a landmark.

24. *Geneva on the Fox River.*—One mile north of course. Two branches of the Chicago & North Western cross each other here at right angles.

84. *Dixon.*—Three miles north of course on Rock River.

96. *Twin Cities of Stirling and Rock Falls.*—One on each side of the Rock River.

130. *Mississippi River.*—The Mississippi River should be crossed about 6 miles below Clinton, Iowa, which is on the west bank of the Mississippi. Flying in the same direction, the Wapsipinacan [Wapsipinicon] River will show up soon after crossing the Mississippi. The Wapsipinacan empties into the Mississippi a few miles south of the course. Fly in the same general direction with this river in view for 24 miles. The Chicago, Rock Island & Pacific runs in the same general direction as this river and is never more than 3 miles from it until Dixon, Iowa, is reached.

154. *Dixon, Iowa.*—One mile north of the course and 1 mile west of the Wapsipinacan River, which turns north at this point. Dixon lies between the Chicago, Rock Island & Pacific and the C. N. W. & St. P., which cross about 1 mile east of Dixon.

173. *Tipton, Iowa.*—Five miles north of the course. Soon after Tipton is reached, Cedar Rapids will be crossed. The Cedar River flows southeast at this point.

191. *Iowa City, Iowa.*—On the eastern bank of the Iowa River. The Chicago Rock Island & Pacific has four lines running out of Iowa City. The air-mail field is south of town and on the western bank of the river. The field is small and is longer east and west.

215. *Chicago, Milwaukee & St. Paul Railway.*

233. *Chicago & North Western Railway.*

240. *Montezuma.*—Directly on course on Minneapolis & St. Louis Railway.

249. *Minneapolis & St. Louis Railway.*

253. *Minneapolis & St. Louis Railway.*—Short line.

255. *Minneapolis & St. Louis Railway.*

271. *Monroe.*—Slightly south of course on Chicago, Rock Island & Pacific Railroad. Three lines out of this town.

296. *Des Moines.*—Five miles north of course. Largest city near course between Iowa City and Omaha. Keep the Raccoon River in sight until about 18 miles out. From here on keep the Chicago, Rock Island & Pacific in sight. This railroad follows the direction of the Raccoon River for this distance. The Chicago, Rock Island & Pacific is 2 to 7 miles north of the course.

368. *Atlantic, Iowa.*—Three miles north of the course on the Chicago, Rock Island & Pacific Railway. At Atlantic the railroads branch in five directions. If on the course at this point, that is, 3 miles south of Atlantic, fly nearly due west until Council Bluffs is seen.

413. *Council Bluffs, Iowa.*—Five miles east of the Missouri River.

418. *Missouri River*, which is very irregular in its course and width at this point.

424. *Omaha, Nebr.*—Field is west of city and can be identified by large hangar with white circle and cross on roof. North of field is large race track and grandstand. There are two good approaches, from north and west.

V

OMAHA TO CHEYENNE

Miles.

0. *Omaha, Nebr.*—The air mail field is on the western outskirts of the city, and is 5 miles west of the Missouri
River. The field is rectangular, the long way of the rec-
tangle being east and west. On the north side of the field
is a long grand stand facing northward and extending
east and west. To the north of the grand stand is a large
field with an elliptical race track in it. This race track is
an excellent landmark, and the oval may be used for
landing if necessary. The west side of the mail field is
bounded by a brook, a few trees, and a railroad track. On
the south the field is bounded by a paved road which
ends to the eastward at the Missouri River. This same
road runs due west for several miles beyond the mail
field. On the south side of the field are some high trees
and a few telephone poles. A private hangar is situated
across the road from the air mail field with the word
"Airdrome" painted on the roof. The air mail hangar is
located in the southeast corner of the field. The east side
of the field is bounded by two steel wireless towers and a
hill covered with high trees. From the northwest is the
best approach, although landings can be made from any
direction if made into the wind.

20. *The Platte River* is crossed at right angles by flying due
west from the Omaha field. By noting section lines the
pilot can determine the correct compass course correct-
ing for drift, as North Platte and Cheyenne are almost
due west of Omaha. For a distance of 70 miles the Platte
River is north of the course never at a greater distance
than 10 miles. The Platte River should be crossed between two bridges, one 2 miles north and the other 2
miles south of the course.

21. *Yutan.*—Directly on the course 1 mile west of the Platte
River, 5 lines of railroads form a junction at this point.

33. *Wahoo.*—A fair-sized town 3 miles south of the course.

Six railroads radiate from Wahoo. An excellent emergency landing field is located one-half mile south of Wahoo; a smooth barley field approximately 1 mile long and a quarter of a mile wide. By noting section lines and flying 25 miles west for each mile south, a direct course may be maintained.

59. *David City.*—A quarter of a mile north of the course. Six railroads radiate from this city also.

82. *Osceola.*—Four miles south of the course. The Union Pacific tracks almost parallel the course from David City to Osceola, where they turn to the southward. Osceola may be identified by a mile race track just south of the town.

96. *The Platte River* is crossed again and runs southwestward. The Union Pacific Railroad is crossed just beyond the Platte River a half a mile north of the small town of Clarks. Twelve miles southwest is Central City on the Union Pacific Railroad. This city is 7 miles south of the course. Central City is directly east of North Platte. If the pilot passes directly over this city, the east-west section lines can be followed directly into North Platte. Thirty-five miles southwest of Clarks is Grand Island in a direct line with Central City. Grand Island is 20 miles south of the course. At Grand Island there is a commercial flying field where supplies of oil and gas may be purchased.

132. *St. Paul, directly on the course.*—Ten miles east of St. Paul one branch of the Chicago, Burlington & Quincy Railroad runs directly west to St. Paul and lies on the course. Five railroads radiate out of St. Paul. The Middle Loup River is crossed 1 mile east of St. Paul.

161. *Loup City.*—Is 5 miles north of the course on the east bank of Middle Loup River, which is crossed almost due south of Loup City. The Union Pacific Railroad paralleling the river is crossed 1 mile east of the river.

176. *The Chicago, Burlington & Quincy Railroad* tracks following a tiny stream are crossed. The railroad runs northwest-southeast at this point.

183. *Mason City.*—On the Chicago, Burlington & Quincy Railroad; is 2 miles north of the course.

216. *The Union Pacific Railroad*, running northeast-southwest, is crossed midway between Lodi and Oconto; Lodi to the north and Oconto to the south. A small creek runs through Oconto which distinguishes it from Lodi.

248. *North Platte.*—After crossing the Union Pacific Railroad no distinguishing landmarks are available, but flying west the Platte River will be seen to the south, gradually getting nearer to the course. The city of North Platte is located at the junction of the north and south branches of the Platte River. The field is located on the east bank of the north branch about 2½ miles east of the town, just 100 yards south of the Lincoln Highway Bridge. Another bridge, the Union Pacific Railroad bridge, crosses the stream a mile farther north. The field is triangular with the hangar at the apex of the triangle and on the bank of the river. The field, which is bounded on the southwest by the river bank and on the north side by a ditch, has an excellent turf covered surface always in a dry condition. The field is longer east and west and the best approach is from the end away from the hangar. Cross field landings should not be attempted near the hangar, as the field is narrow at this point. The altitude of North Platte is 2,800 feet or about 2,000 feet higher than the Omaha field.

298. *Ogallala.*—The south branch of the Platte River parallels the course to this point and the north branch is only a mile or two north of the course, veering gradually to the northward. The double tracks of the Union Pacific Railroad follow the course to this point. Fly directly west from this point, the south branch of the Platte River and the Union Pacific Railroad, veering to the southward.

338. *Chappell.*—Two miles south of the course on the Union Pacific tracks and on the north bank of the Lodgepole Creek.

342. *Lodgepole.*—Directly on the course between the Union Pacific Railroad and Lodgepole Creek. From here on to

Sidney the course lies over the Union Pacific Railroad tracks and Lodgepole Creek.

360. *Sidney.*—The Union Pacific double track runs through here east and west, crossed at right angles by the Chicago, Burlington & Quincy Railroad running north and south. Two miles west of Sidney the Union Pacific double track veers to the north, following the course of the Lodgepole Creek. The course, due west, lies from 4 to 6 miles south of the railroad and creek for the next 60 miles.

395. *Kimball.*—Five miles north of the course on the Union Pacific Railroad and Lodgepole Creek.

420. *Pine Bluff.*—On the Union Pacific Railroad 2 miles north of the course. The railroad and creek again cross the course, the railroad, turning westward to Cheyenne and the creek, continuing south for 4 miles and then eastward. The country between Sidney and Pine Bluff is the roughest on the whole course from Omaha to Cheyenne, but plenty of emergency fields are found. A ridge extends southward from Pine Bluff, on which numerous dark green trees may be seen. Two miles southwest of Pine Bluff the Union Pacific tracks are crossed and for 5 miles lie south of the course. Then another intersection of the course and the railroad looping to the northward and again crossing the course at the small town of Archer.

499. *Archer.*—A small town on the Union Pacific Railroad and 8 miles from Cheyenne.

458. *Cheyenne.*—Can be identified by the barracks of Fort Russell. The Cheyenne field is three-quarters of a mile due north of the town and due north of the capitol building, whose gilded dome is unmistakable. The field, though rolling, is very large and landings may be made from any direction. A pilot landing here for the first time must "watch his step," as the rarified atmosphere at this altitude (6,100 feet) makes rough landings the rule rather than the exception.

V I

CHEYENNE TO SALT LAKE

Two descriptions are given of this route from Cheyenne to Rock Springs, the following being the shorter:

Miles.

0. *Cheyenne.*—A white hangar, small white office building, and the wireless towers are on the southwest corner of the field. Field is extensive and the surface is hard. Fly over Fort Russell and follow the Colorado & Southern tracks to Federal.

12. *Federal.*—The first town on the Colorado & Southern tracks after it [they] makes a sharp bend to the north. From here almost directly west will be seen black irregular peaks in the Laramie Mountains. Fly over the mountains just to the north of these peaks. This will bring you into the Laramie Valley about due east of Laramie.

40. *Laramie.*—Is the largest town in this valley. Landing fields abound throughout the valley.

61. *Sheep Mountains.*—The flat top of these mountains resembles a huddled-up bunch of sheep. A short range about 10 miles long. Pass to the north of the mountains and fly due west over the Medicine Bow Range.

77. *Medicine Bow Range.*—Extending north and south. Cross this range at right angles and you come out into the valley of the North Platte River. Landing fields abound throughout this valley. To the west may be seen the Sierra Madre Range. Identified by high, white peaks, with the range extending southeast-northwest. Pass to the north of the mountainous part of this range where the rounded hills are covered with dense pine forests. From here fly about 7° north of west, compass course. You will pass over a rather high and dry plateau cut up by irregular canyons, but with a number of landing fields that can be reached from an 8,000-foot altitude. Continue westward, veering to the north until the tracks of the Union Pacific Railroad are seen to the north. Cross the Union

Pacific tracks to the north of Black Buttes, a small town on the Union Pacific; ahead will be seen an irregular butte known as Black Butte. Pass to the north of this and the Aspen Mountains will be seen to the southwest and the Table Mountain Range to the west and a little north. The top of Table Mountain Range is almost flat with the exception of Pilot Butte. This is a symmetrical, flat top butte on the top of the range. Fly directly toward Pilot Butte. This will take you over a dry sandy valley across the Union Pacific tracks near Baxter over a low range of hills to the Rock Springs landing field.

The following description does not follow the direct course and is about 10 miles farther than the route described previously. The country over this course is better suited for forced landings, and in case of a forced landing the pilot is nearer human habitation.

Miles.

0. *Cheyenne.*—Fly west over or to the north of Fort Russell, which is about 4 miles from town, following the Colorado & Southern tracks to the point where they bend sharply to the north.

12. *Federal.*—The first town on the Colorado & Southern Railroad after the railroad makes a sharp bend to the north. Fly about 6 miles south of Federal and leave the Colorado & Southern tracks about 1 mile north of the pronounced bend. The compass course, when there is no cross wind, is about 310°. Cross Sherman Hills or Laramie Mountains at about 9,000 feet above sea level. Crossing this range of mountains the Laramie Valley appears, where landing fields abound.

40. *Laramie.*—On the Union Pacific double-tracked railroad. The largest town in the valley. Pass 6 miles to the north of Laramie.

60. *Rock River.*—On the Union Pacific, 20 miles north of the course. The double-tracked Union Pacific passes through 2 miles of snow sheds at this point.

80. *Elk Mountain.*—To the north of the Medicine Bow

Range, a black and white range of mountains, the black parts of which are forests and the white snow-covered rocks. Elk Mountain is 12,500 feet high. Fly to the north of this conspicuous mountain over high, rough country. The Union Pacific tracks will be seen about 15 miles to the north gradually converging with the course.

114. *Walcott.*—Cross the S. & E. Railroad 2 miles south of Walcott. The S. & E. joins the Union Pacific at this point.

134. *Rawlins.*—Follow the general direction of the Union Pacific tracks to Rawlins, which is on the Union Pacific tracks. The country between Walcott and Rawlins is fairly level, but covered with sage brush, which makes landings dangerous. Rawlins is on the north side of the Union Pacific tracks at a point about a mile east of where the tracks cut through a low ridge of hills. Large railroad shops distinguish the town. The emergency field provided here lies about 1¼ miles northeast of town at the base of a large hill. Landings are made almost invariably to the west. Surface of field is fairly good, as the sage brush has been removed. Easily identified by this, as the surrounding country is covered with sage brush. Landings can be made in any direction into the wind if care is exercised. Several ranch buildings and two small black shacks on the eastern side of the field help distinguish it. Leaving Rawlins follow the Union Pacific tracks to Creston.

159. *Creston.*—A small station on the Union Pacific is the point where the course crosses the Continental Divide.

175. *Wamsutter.*—On the Union Pacific. Fairly good fields are found between Rawlins and a point 60 miles west. Fields safe to land in show up on account of the absence of sage brush. The course leaves the railroad where the Union Pacific tracks loop to the southeast.

215. *Black Butte.*—A huge black hill of rock south of the course. The Union Pacific Railroad is crossed just before reaching Black Butte.

231. *Rock Springs.*—After passing Black Butte, Pilot Butte will be seen projecting above and forming a part of the Table Mountain Range. This butte is of whitish stone.

PILOTS' DIRECTIONS

Head directly toward Pilot Butte and Rock Springs will be passed on the northern side. The field is in the valley at the foot of Pilot Butte about 4 miles from Rock Springs. It is triangular in shape, the hangar being located in the apex. The surface of the field is good. The best approach is from the eastern side.

246. *Green River.*—Follow the Union Pacific double-tracked railroad from Rock Springs. There is an emergency field here which is distinguished [on] account of its being the only cleared space of its size, near the town. Green river is crossed immediately after the city of Green River is passed. Here the course leaves the railroad which continues in a northwesterly direction. By flying approximately 230° compass course from here, Cheyenne [Salt Lake City] will be reached.

258. *Black Fork River.*—A very irregular river, which is crossed at right angles. From Black Fork to Coalville the Union Pacific tracks are from 5 to 20 miles north of the course.

282. *Granger.*—16 miles north of the course on the Union Pacific where the Oregon Short Line joins the Union Pacific from the north.

330. *Altamont.*—On the Union Pacific where the Union Pacific approaches within 6 miles of the course to the north. The railroad passes through a short tunnel at this point.

338. *Evanston.*—After approaching within 6 miles of the course, the railroad turns sharply to the northwest. Evanston is on the Union Pacific 18 miles north of the course. There is a good emergency landing field on the southwest side of Evanston, a mile from the railroad station. From Evanston the Union Pacific tracks curve toward the course until Coalville is reached.

363. *Coalville.*—On the single track Union Pacific running north and south. The single track Union Pacific joins the double track 4 miles north of Coalville at Echo City. There is an emergency landing field here a mile east of the railroad and one-half mile southeast of town. There is a marker on this field.

381. *Salt Lake City.*—From Coalville the country is extremely rugged and the pilot should maintain at least 11,000 feet altitude above sea level. The field lies 2 miles west of the city on the north side of the road or street which extends east-west by the Salt Lake fair grounds. Locate the fair grounds, identified by an elliptical race track and large buildings. Follow westward along the road just south of the fair grounds and the field will be reached 1½ miles farther on. The field is about one-half mile long north and south and landings are usually made in one of these directions. A landing T is used to indicate the proper place to land. Elevation here is 4,400 feet. High-tension wires border all sides of the field except the north.

V I I

SALT LAKE CITY TO RENO

Miles.

0. *Salt Lake City.*—Fly west from Salt Lake, keeping the two railroads running due west from Salt Lake to the south.

12. *Saltair.*—Near the salt works there is an open field which is possible for an emergency landing. The field lies between the highway and the electric railroad that runs into Salt Lake City. Is rolling and covered sparsely with sagebrush and should be used only in case of absolute emergency.

14. *Antelope Island.*—In the Great Salt Lake, 6 miles north of the course.

30. *Stansbury Island.*—In the Great Salt Lake. The course crosses this island about 2 miles from its southern edge.

45. *The Union Pacific Railroad* is crossed where it runs northeast-southwest. Two miles north of the course the railroad makes a sharp bend and runs southeast-northwest.

50. *The Union Pacific Railroad* is crossed again. The Union Pacific continues southeast from here for 10 miles and then turns westward and parallels the course to Wendover. The course is 6 miles north of the railroad.

98. *Salduro.*—On the Union Pacific Railroad, 6 miles south of the course. There is an emergency field here in vat No. 5, marked by a black T. The vat is circular, 400 feet in diameter and the bottom, composed of white salt, is hard as a pavement.

108. *Wendover.*—On the Union Pacific, 6 miles south of the course. Opposite the Conley Hotel and the Union Pacific station there is a landing field L-shaped, 1,200 feet long each way and 600 feet wide, a good emergency field. Four miles west of Wendover the Union Pacific Railroad turns to the north and east and is crossed 8 miles west of Wendover. The railroad continues northwestward and reaches a northern point 11 miles from the course. The

railroad curves and runs southeast, where it crosses the Nevada Northern, running north-south at Shafter.

130. *Shafter.*—At the junction of the Nevada Northern and Western Pacific Railroads. Opposite the Western Pacific station at Shafter there is a stretch of ground 1,200 feet wide and unlimited in extent the long way, that may be used for emergency landings. There is a scattering of sagebrush on this field.

145. *The Western Pacific Railroad* is crossed, running northwest-southeast, after it makes a loop to the south just beyond Shafter. The railroad veers to the north until it is 20 miles north of the course.

157. *Snow Water Lake.*—An oblong body of water 3 miles south of the course. The long way of the lake extends parallel to the course.

170. *Secret Pass in the East Humboldt Range.*—The only pass in this range for many miles. Some peaks in this range attain an altitude of more than 12,000 feet. The northern extremity of the Ruby Range extending north and south lies a few miles south of the course and is next seen. Then three branches of Tamoville Creek flowing north to the east fork of the Humboldt River are crossed at short intervals. The Southern Pacific and Western Pacific Railroads follow the course of the east fork of the Humboldt River and gradually converge on the course where all four join at Elko.

204. *Elko.*—Lies in the Humboldt Valley. The air mail field is 1 mile west of the city, with the main runway east and west. Landings may be made from any direction, although it is advisable to land east and west. There is a ditch at the east end of the field. Follow the general direction of the railroad tracks out of Elko, as they run parallel with the course for several miles.

224. *Carlin.*—Between the Western Pacific and the Southern Pacific Railroad tracks, 1 mile south of the course.

238. *Harney.*—Six miles south of the course, midway between the cities of Palisade and Beowawe on the Southern Pacific and Western Pacific Railroads. South of the

railroad tracks here is an emergency field 1,500 by 900 feet, with a shallow ditch in the center running across. Landings can be made safely across this ditch. There is a ranch house in one corner of the field. A narrow gauge railroad runs south from Palisade, a town 7 miles east of Harney.

246. The course crosses the Western Pacific and Southern Pacific Railroad tracks. Up to this time the railroad tracks have been on the south of the course, but from now on the two railroads are to the north.

268. *Battle Mountain.*—At the junction of the Southern Pacific and the Nevada Central Railroads, 8 miles north of the course. Battle Mountain lies in a valley surrounded on the east and west by high ranges. Here will be found an excellent landing field laid out in the form of an ellipse, marked with a T and a wind-indicator. The field lies directly west of town. All types of supplies for servicing may be found here. From this point the railroads turn north and west and leave the course almost at right angles.

278. *The Nevada Central Railroad* is crossed 12 miles southwest of Battle Mountain. From here on for the next 100 miles the course lies over uninhabited and desert country.

293. *Alkali Lake.*—Lies on the northern edge of the course.

363. *Humboldt Lake.*—The course adjoins the southern edge of this lake and crosses the Southern Pacific Railroad 5 miles beyond. If the pilot elects to not fly the direct course, the Southern Pacific Railroad may be followed from Battle Mountain to Winnemucca, a distance of approximately 60 miles. At Winnemucca is an emergency field south of town, marked by a wind indicator and a T. Supplies necessary for reservicing a ship may be obtained here. At this point the Western Pacific continues on in a westward direction, while the Southern Pacific turns to the southwest. Following the Southern Pacific for 30 miles the small town of Imlay will be reached. There is open unobstructed land on all sides of

this town, suitable for emergency landings. Forty miles farther on will be found the city of Lovelocks. A first-class landing field is situated here on the eastern edge of the Southern Pacific tracks just south of town. A permanent T has been placed on the field and a rolled runway constructed. Gas and oil may be obtained from the Standard Oil plant on the edge of the field, and at a near-by fertilizer plant there is a fully-equipped machine shop which is offered for the use of any pilot who may need to make repairs to his ship. This field is level and is kept up in good shape. Pilots coming in must hold the ship up with the gun until they pass over a series of irrigation ditches at the end of the field. After these ditches have been passed a landing may be made. Numerous emergency landing fields may be found all the way between Winnemucca and Lovelocks. Twenty-five miles farther on the Southern Pacific joins the course 5 miles east of the southern edge of Humboldt Lake, into which the Humboldt River empties. To the south of Lake Humboldt is Carson Sink, which has a dry sandy bottom throughout the year and offers an ideal landing ground, but is uninhabited and pilots can not receive assistance except along the railroad. By following the Southern Pacific Railroad from Humboldt Lake southward for 25 miles, Hazen, Nev., will be reached.

388. *Hazen, Nev.*—Fourteen miles south of the course on the Southern Pacific Railroad. Four branches of this railroad radiate out of Hazen. All about the town there are open fields of a size sufficient to set down an airplane. The best landing field is to the south and east of the Southern Pacific roundhouse and is a space a mile long and half a mile wide. Sagebrush grows on the eastern portion of this field and the southern end is bounded by a set of high-tension wires. A 40-foot T marks the field. If the pilot has flown as far south as Hazen he can follow the Southern Pacific westward into Reno. If he is on the direct course, he will cross the northern branch of the Southern Pacific 7 miles north of where it joins the east-

west main line at Fernley. Twelve miles to the north Pyramid Lake can be seen.

437. *Reno, Nev.*—The air mail field at Reno lies 2 miles west of the city. The main runway is east and west. The field is marked by a T and wind indicator, and landing from four ways is unobstructed. Reno is 4,497 feet above sea level. Whenever possible it is advisable to leave the Reno field on the east-west runway, taking off to the east. A slight downgrade enables the ship to quickly obtain flying speed. Just beyond the east edge of the field the ground is extremely rough and there is a huge ditch here.

V I I I

RENO TO SAN FRANCISCO

0. Leaving the Reno field the pilot should head his ship southwest and gain altitude of at least 10,000 feet to pass safely over the Sierras. Practically all of this altitude should be obtained near the field before starting on the course.

20. *Lake Tahoe.*—The northern edge of Lake Tahoe is 6 miles south of the course.

25. *Truckee.*—On the Southern Pacific near the point where Lake Tahoe Railway joins the Southern Pacific from the south. Two and a half miles to the northwest of Truckee lies a very good summertime emergency landing field. All approaches are clear and a space available for a landing 600 by 2,000 feet. A big bowlder painted white stands on the northwest side of the field and beside it is a white wind indicator. This field is to be avoided in winter, as snow gathers on it to a frequent depth of 4 feet. Soon after passing Truckee the Sierras are crossed. On the direct course 10,000 feet will clear the highest peak, but an altitude of 15,000 feet should be maintained. The Southern Pacific Railroad tracks veer to the west and north and from here on to Sacramento are at a varying distance of 5 to 20 miles north and west of the course.

65. *Colfax.*—Seventeen miles northwest of the course on the Southern Pacific Railroad. Elevation here is 2,422 feet. A small level field lies one-half mile south of the city. The field should be used only in an emergency, as it is difficult to get into and during the rainy season is very soft. The field is 600 by 300 feet.

85. *Shingle Springs.*—Seven miles south and east of the course, on the Placerville Branch of the Southern Pacific that runs from Placerville to Sacramento. There is a field here one-half mile west of Shingle Springs, bounded on the north by a highway running to Placerville and on the

south by the Southern Pacific tracks. The field is 1,500 yards long north and south and 300 yards wide east and west. The ground is level, hard, and smooth. The elevation here is approximately 1,000 feet.

95. *The Southern Pacific*, running from Placerville to Sacramento, is crossed at right angles 1 mile southeast of where it makes a right-angular bend and approximately parallels the course for the next 15 miles. The course lies from 1 to 3 miles southeast of this track.

112. *Mather Field.*—Is the Army Air Service station in the Sacramento Valley, equipped like all Air Service flying fields. It is located to the east of Sacramento and near the small siding called Mills, 2 miles north and east of the course. A huge white water tower serves as an excellent landmark as well as the three lines of buildings on the ground. Three railroads are crossed in a stretch of less than 10 miles soon after leaving Mather Field. The Southern Pacific Railroad is to the northeast of the course at a varying distance of 10 to 15 miles after leaving Mather Field. Southwest of the course the Sacramento River will be seen soon after crossing the three railroad tracks at a distance of 5 to 10 miles.

152. *Suison [Suisun] Bay.*—Into which the Sacramento River empties, a large oblong body of water parallel to the course. The pilot will fly along the southwest side of this bay.

162. *Martinez.*—On the southeast corner of Suison bay. One mile northwest of the course.

177. *Durant Field, Oakland, Calif.*—On the eastern side of San Francisco Bay. The field runs almost due east and west and has a hangar, wind indicator, and T laid out on it. By coming in from the east over the hangar an unobstructed run of about 2,000 feet is obtained. North and south the field is rather narrow and somewhat rough. All supplies necessary for reservicing a ship may be obtained here. From here fly directly across San Francisco Bay. The course goes directly over Alcatraz Island, cov-

PILOTS' DIRECTIONS

ered with white Government buildings. Goat Island, larger than Alcatraz, and more irregularly shaped, on which is located the Naval Station to be seen to the south.

187. *Marina Field.*—Is stationed on the south of San Francisco Bay, 3 miles from the Golden Gate, on the east portion of the old fair grounds. It can be identified by the Palace of Fine Arts Building, which has a large dome roof, at the west end of the field; a monument 150 feet high, the Column of Progress, is on the north side of the field. The city of San Francisco is to the south. There is a prevailing southwest wind here. A double line of wires borders the eastern edge of the field and this, in conjunction with the gas plant in the same vicinity, forces the pilot to come in high. The pilot should hold the ship off until the runway is reached coming in either direction, as both the east and west edges of the field are very rough. Landings should not be attempted from any direction other than the east and west.

INDEX

I N D E X

I N D E X

I N D E X